Resource Book

ALGEBRA

Structure and Method,   Book 1

Dolciani · Brown · Cole

Printed in U.S.A.
ISBN: 0-395-35256-8

ABCDEFGHIJ-WC-93210/898765

HOUGHTON MIFFLIN COMPANY · BOSTON
Atlanta · Dallas · Geneva, Ill. · Lawrenceville, N.J. · Palo Alto · Toronto

Contents

This Resource Book has been designed to make your teaching easier by providing a source of extra tests, practice exercises, and enrichment material—all keyed to the student textbook. Teachers are granted permission to duplicate these materials for classroom use with their students. A brief description of the different kinds of materials included follows.

Guide to Tests, Practice Exercises, Mixed Review, Enrichment Activities, and Problem Solving Worksheets

For use after Section	Tests	Practice Exercises	Mixed Review	Enrichment Activities	Problem Solving
1-2		p. 67			
1-6		p. 68			
1-9		p. 69			
Chap. 1	pp. 5, 7			p. 145	
2-3		p. 70			
2-5		p. 71			
2-7		p. 72			
2-9		p. 73			
Chap. 2	pp. 9, 11			p. 146	
3-3		p. 74			
3-5		p. 75			
3-6					p. 161
3-7					p. 163
3-8		p. 76			
Chap. 3	pp. 13, 15			p. 149	
Cum. Rev. Chaps. 1-3	p. 17	p. 77	p. 133		
4-2		p. 79			
4-4		p. 80			
4-6		p. 81			
4-8		p. 82			p. 165
4-9					p. 169

(continued on page 202)

Diagnostic Tests in Arithmetic

Whole Numbers

1. Addition

1. $\begin{array}{r} 63 \\ +\ 35 \\ \hline \end{array}$	**2.** $\begin{array}{r} 98 \\ +\ \ 2 \\ \hline \end{array}$	**3.** $\begin{array}{r} 64 \\ +\ 27 \\ \hline \end{array}$	**4.** $\begin{array}{r} 29 \\ +\ 35 \\ \hline \end{array}$	**5.** $\begin{array}{r} 58 \\ 41 \\ +\ 50 \\ \hline \end{array}$
6. $\begin{array}{r} 97 \\ 88 \\ +\ 92 \\ \hline \end{array}$	**7.** $\begin{array}{r} 73 \\ 69 \\ 34 \\ +\ 95 \\ \hline \end{array}$	**8.** $\begin{array}{r} 460 \\ 84 \\ +\ 907 \\ \hline \end{array}$	**9.** $\begin{array}{r} 10,009 \\ 326 \\ 9,876 \\ +\ \ 4,039 \\ \hline \end{array}$	**10.** $\begin{array}{r} 427 \\ 2476 \\ 9009 \\ +\ \ 576 \\ \hline \end{array}$

2. Subtraction

1. $\begin{array}{r} 95 \\ -\ 64 \\ \hline \end{array}$	**2.** $\begin{array}{r} 83 \\ -\ 29 \\ \hline \end{array}$	**3.** $\begin{array}{r} 57 \\ -\ 49 \\ \hline \end{array}$	**4.** $\begin{array}{r} 96 \\ -\ 38 \\ \hline \end{array}$	**5.** $\begin{array}{r} 728 \\ -\ 305 \\ \hline \end{array}$
6. $\begin{array}{r} 805 \\ -\ 207 \\ \hline \end{array}$	**7.** $\begin{array}{r} 932 \\ -\ 239 \\ \hline \end{array}$	**8.** $\begin{array}{r} 6403 \\ -\ 5099 \\ \hline \end{array}$	**9.** $\begin{array}{r} 9987 \\ -\ 3088 \\ \hline \end{array}$	**10.** $\begin{array}{r} 16,475 \\ -\ \ 9,679 \\ \hline \end{array}$

3. Multiplication

1. $\begin{array}{r} 46 \\ \times\ \ 2 \\ \hline \end{array}$	**2.** $\begin{array}{r} 58 \\ \times\ \ 4 \\ \hline \end{array}$	**3.** $\begin{array}{r} 39 \\ \times\ 20 \\ \hline \end{array}$	**4.** $\begin{array}{r} 64 \\ \times\ 70 \\ \hline \end{array}$	**5.** $\begin{array}{r} 98 \\ \times\ 23 \\ \hline \end{array}$
6. $\begin{array}{r} 67 \\ \times\ 42 \\ \hline \end{array}$	**7.** $\begin{array}{r} 182 \\ \times\ \ 63 \\ \hline \end{array}$	**8.** $\begin{array}{r} 204 \\ \times\ \ 13 \\ \hline \end{array}$	**9.** $\begin{array}{r} 6081 \\ \times\ 4000 \\ \hline \end{array}$	**10.** $\begin{array}{r} 8392 \\ \times\ \ 408 \\ \hline \end{array}$

4. Division

Express remainders as fractions.

1. $439 \div 3$	**2.** $921 \div 4$	**3.** $1520 \div 6$	**4.** $12\overline{)8360}$	**5.** $23\overline{)4006}$
6. $18\overline{)2095}$	**7.** $29\overline{)6087}$	**8.** $305\overline{)2250}$	**9.** $168\overline{)9876}$	**10.** $1239 \div 433$

ALGEBRA, Structure and Method, Book 1

Diagnostic Tests in Arithmetic

Decimals

1. Addition

(a) Estimate the sum by rounding each addend to the highest place value.
(b) Find the actual sum.

1.	**2.**	**3.**	**4.**	**5.**
4.6	10.23	29.2	6.79	13.14
5.9	4.9	1.9	0.73	928.2
+ 15.1	+ 6.15	+ 15.9	+ 0.205	+ 4.16

6.	**7.**	**8.**	**9.**	**10.**
0.4	$536.10	7.77	$3.50	0.75
6.356	8.90	5.6	9.50	0.25
0.9	29.00	16.49	8.37	0.42
+ 6.43	+ 366.40	+ 0.9	+ 3.69	28.3
				+ 6.4

2. Subtraction

1.	**2.**	**3.**	**4.**	**5.**
18.75	29.84	$30.50	3.1416	$6.245
− 13.25	− 6.95	− 1.98	− 1.09	− 5.735

6.	**7.**	**8.**	**9.**	**10.**
686.5	92	76.3	8705.56	3900.04
− 87	− 3.25	− 9.14	− 970.64	− 23.09

3. Multiplication

1.	**2.**	**3.**	**4.**	**5.**
$3.75	$6.15	40.9	63.6	0.07
× 6	× 39	× 1.3	× 4.2	× 0.3

6.	**7.**	**8.**	**9.**	**10.**
0.09	10.36	9.365	3.1416	4.7659
× 0.06	× 4.8	× 3.07	× 0.5	× 21.2

4. Division

Give quotients to the nearest tenth.

1. $9\overline{)81.9}$ **2.** $7\overline{)81.9}$ **3.** $0.6\overline{)8.19}$ **4.** $10 \div 3$ **5.** $125 \div 7$

6. $931 \div 8$ **7.** $2.5\overline{)0.376}$ **8.** $1.7\overline{)1.000}$ **9.** $0.09\overline{)337}$ **10.** $0.97 \div 3.999$

ALGEBRA, Structure and Method, Book 1

Diagnostic Tests in Arithmetic

Fractions

1. Basic Ideas

Write the numerator.

1. $\dfrac{2}{7}$ 2. $\dfrac{4}{9}$ 3. $\dfrac{3}{4}$ 4. $\dfrac{9}{10}$

Write the denominator.

5. $\dfrac{3}{8}$ 6. $\dfrac{4}{3}$ 7. $\dfrac{10}{2}$ 8. $\dfrac{1}{100}$

Write the GCF of the denominators.

9. $\dfrac{2}{3}, \dfrac{1}{9}$ 10. $\dfrac{1}{2}, \dfrac{1}{10}, \dfrac{1}{20}$ 11. $\dfrac{1}{21}, \dfrac{1}{84}$ 12. $\dfrac{5}{42}, \dfrac{7}{49}, \dfrac{10}{84}$

Write in lowest terms.

13. $\dfrac{3}{21}$ 14. $\dfrac{50}{125}$ 15. $\dfrac{65}{225}$ 16. $\dfrac{36}{81}$

Write as a mixed number in lowest terms.

17. $\dfrac{20}{3}$ 18. $\dfrac{81}{10}$ 19. $\dfrac{34}{16}$ 20. $\dfrac{225}{50}$

Compare. Write =, <, or > in place of ?.

21. $1\frac{3}{5} ? \dfrac{8}{5}$ 22. $\dfrac{1}{7} ? \dfrac{1}{8}$ 23. $\dfrac{3}{4} ? \dfrac{11}{16}$ 24. $4\frac{1}{2} ? \dfrac{64}{16}$

25. $\dfrac{3}{8} ? \dfrac{1}{2}$ 26. $1\frac{8}{9} ? \dfrac{64}{32}$

Write as a decimal, rounded to tenths.

27. $\dfrac{3}{4}$ - 28. $\dfrac{7}{8}$ 29. $\dfrac{3}{16}$ 30. $\dfrac{1}{3}$

Write as a fraction or mixed number.

31. 0.8 32. 0.75 33. 1.6 34. 1.875

(continued)

ALGEBRA, Structure and Method, Book 1

Diagnostic Tests in Arithmetic

2. Addition

Write answers in lowest terms.

1. $\dfrac{1}{4} + \dfrac{1}{3}$ 2. $\dfrac{1}{8} + \dfrac{1}{2}$ 3. $\dfrac{3}{4} + \dfrac{5}{12}$ 4. $\dfrac{1}{6} + \dfrac{2}{3}$ 5. $3\frac{1}{4} + 5\frac{1}{8}$

6. $16\frac{1}{9} + \dfrac{2}{3}$
7. $\begin{array}{r} 14\frac{1}{2} \\ + \ 3\frac{7}{8} \\ \hline \end{array}$
8. $\begin{array}{r} 2\frac{5}{6} \\ + \ 10\frac{1}{3} \\ \hline \end{array}$
9. $\begin{array}{r} 12\frac{1}{6} \\ + \ 5\frac{1}{8} \\ \hline \end{array}$

3. Subtraction

Write answers in lowest terms.

1. $\dfrac{3}{8} - \dfrac{1}{4}$ 2. $\dfrac{3}{16} - \dfrac{1}{8}$ 3. $\dfrac{5}{12} - \dfrac{1}{6}$ 4. $\dfrac{2}{3} - \dfrac{1}{8}$ 5. $1\frac{1}{2} - \dfrac{1}{7}$

6. $15\frac{1}{4} - 11\frac{5}{8}$
7. $\begin{array}{r} 10\frac{1}{2} \\ - \ 8\frac{4}{5} \\ \hline \end{array}$
8. $\begin{array}{r} 16\frac{3}{10} \\ - \ 11\frac{3}{8} \\ \hline \end{array}$
9. $\begin{array}{r} 25\frac{1}{8} \\ - \ 10\frac{5}{6} \\ \hline \end{array}$

4. Multiplication

Write answers in lowest terms.

1. $2 \times \dfrac{3}{7}$ 2. $\dfrac{1}{2} \times \dfrac{3}{7}$ 3. $14 \times \dfrac{2}{7}$ 4. $\dfrac{5}{12} \times \dfrac{4}{5}$ 5. $\dfrac{3}{4} \times \dfrac{4}{21}$

6. $4\frac{1}{2} \times \dfrac{1}{2}$ 7. $3\frac{1}{7} \times \dfrac{1}{3}$ 8. $16\frac{1}{2} \times \dfrac{1}{4}$ 9. $1\frac{3}{8} \times 2\frac{1}{2}$

5. Division

Write answers in lowest terms.

1. $\dfrac{1}{2} \div \dfrac{1}{8}$ 2. $\dfrac{3}{4} \div \dfrac{3}{16}$ 3. $\dfrac{5}{12} \div \dfrac{1}{4}$ 4. $3\frac{1}{8} \div \dfrac{1}{3}$ 5. $6\frac{1}{2} \div \dfrac{1}{4}$

6. $8\frac{1}{3} \div \dfrac{1}{6}$ 7. $1\frac{2}{3} \div 1\frac{1}{2}$ 8. $8\frac{1}{4} \div 1\frac{3}{8}$ 9. $7\frac{1}{2} \div 3\dfrac{3}{4}$

6. Ratios

Write the ratio as a fraction in lowest terms.

1. 3 to 5   2. 2 to 6   3. 8 to 24   4. 6:4   5. 6:8

6. 5:100   7. 10 to 2   8. 9:27   9. 80 to 1000

Diagnostic Tests in Arithmetic

Percent

1. Percents and decimals

Write as a percent.

1. 0.15   **2.** 0.65   **3.** 0.01   **4.** 0.07   **5.** 0.255   **6.** 0.166

7. 2.5   **8.** 5.75

Write as a decimal.

9. 10%   **10.** 5%   **11.** 75%   **12.** 100%   **13.** 58%

14. 1.5%   **15.** 10.75%   **16.** 10.8%

2. Percents and fractions

Write as a fraction in lowest terms.

1. 10%   **2.** 50%   **3.** 18%   **4.** 98%   **5.** 5.5%   **6.** 10.2%

7. 7.08%   **8.** 150%

Write as a percent.

9. $\dfrac{1}{2}$ **10.** $\dfrac{1}{4}$ **11.** $\dfrac{1}{6}$ **12.** $\dfrac{3}{4}$ **13.** $\dfrac{1}{8}$ **14.** $\dfrac{7}{8}$ **15.** $\dfrac{4}{5}$ **16.** $\dfrac{9}{25}$

3. Percent Problems

Supply the missing number.

1. 10% of 100 = __?__   **2.** 14% of 50 = __?__   **3.** 50% of 75 = __?__

4. 75% of 16 = __?__   **5.** __?__% of 30 = 3   **6.** __?__% of 75 = 25

7. __?__% of 1000 = 10   **8.** __?__% of 12.5 = $1\frac{1}{4}$ **9.** 40% of __?__ = 12

10. 80% of __?__ = 80   **11.** 1.5% of __?__ = 76   **12.** $33\frac{1}{3}$% of __?__ = 13

ALGEBRA, Structure and Method, Book 1

Test 1—Test on Chapter 1 (Form A)

Directions: Write answers in the spaces provided.

Questions 1–4. Simplify.

1. $(2 \times 3 - 12 \div 3) \div 2$

2. $6(6 + 8) + 8 - 32 \div 16$

3. $30 - 3(7 - 2)$

4. $\dfrac{4(3 + 1) - 1}{4 + 1}$

Questions 5–8. Evaluate if $x = 1$, $y = 3$, $z = 12$, $u = 0$, $v = 5$, and $w = \dfrac{1}{2}$.

5. $2(3x + y)$

6. $3u(z - 2y)$

7. $\dfrac{6w + 5x}{7v}$

8. $8w - x\left(\dfrac{z}{y + 1}\right)$

Questions 9–12. Give the solution set for each open sentence if $x \in \{0, 2, 4, 6, 8\}$.

9. $2x + 1 = 5$

10. $4x < 20$

11. $x - \dfrac{x}{2} = 3$

12. $|x| + 2 = -6$

Questions 13–14. Write an equation that represents the given facts. *Do not solve.*

13. Ten is three less than $\dfrac{1}{2}x$.

14. The sum of x and y, decreased by their product, is 52.

Questions 15–17. Solve, using the five-step plan.

15. If 2 is added to twice a number, the result is 60. Find the number.

16. If Gina had 12 more record albums, she would have 30 albums. How many albums does she have?

17. The number of bolts produced daily by machine A is 300 less than three times the number produced by machine B. If machine A has an output of 4800 bolts per day, what is the daily output of machine B?

ANSWERS

1. _____ (4)
2. _____ (4)
3. _____ (4)
4. _____ (4)
5. _____ (4)
6. _____ (4)
7. _____ (4)
8. _____ (4)
9. _____ (5)
10. _____ (5)
11. _____ (5)
12. _____ (5)
13. _____ (4)
14. _____ (4)
15. _____ (5)
16. _____ (5)
17. _____ (6)

(continued)

Test 1—Test on Chapter 1   *(continued)*

Questions 18–20. Refer to the number line below. Write the coordinate of the point described.

18. The point halfway between C and F

19. The point two-thirds of the distance from E to B

20. The point 1.5 units to the right of D

Questions 21–23. Simplify.

21. $|3| + |-16|$ **22.** $|-12| \cdot |-7|$ **23.** $-(|-15| - |-12|)$

Questions 24–25. Replace each __?__ with $<$, $=$, or $>$ to make a true statement.

24. $|6| - |-2|$ __?__ $|6 + 2|$ **25.** $7(|-3|)$ __?__ $3(|-7|)$

ANSWERS

18. _____ (3)

19. _____ (3)

20. _____ (3)

21. _____ (3)

22. _____ (3)

23. _____ (3)

24. _____ (3)

25. _____ (3)

CHALLENGE ANSWER

_____

CHALLENGE *(Optional)* The sum of Desi's age and Maria's age is 21. Three years ago, Maria was twice as old as Desi. How old is Maria now?

ALGEBRA, Structure and Method, Book 1

Test 2—Test on Chapter 1 (Form B)

Directions: Write answers in the spaces provided.

Questions 1–4. Simplify.

1. $6(7 + 2) - 15 \div 3$

2. $(15 - 3 + 8 \div 2) \div 8 \times 5$

3. $\dfrac{15 \div 3 + 2 \times 3}{2(5 + 6)}$

4. $7 + 3(5 - 1) \div 6$

Questions 5–8. Evaluate if $r = \dfrac{1}{2}$, $s = 4$, $t = 10$, $a = 0$, $b = 1$, and $c = 8$.

5. $tc - 5ar$

6. $\dfrac{3b + t}{5s - t}$

7. $\dfrac{4t + 3s}{4}$

8. $6r + s\left(\dfrac{t}{c - 3}\right)$

Questions 9–12. Give the solution set for each open sentence if $m \in \{1, 3, 5, 7, 9\}$.

9. $20 > 3m + 1$

10. $2m + 7 = 17$

11. $|m| + |-2| = -7$

12. $6 + m = 3m$

Questions 13–14. Write an equation that represents the given facts. *Do not solve.*

13. Twenty-eight is two more than twice m.

14. The sum of a and b, increased by their product, is 55.

Questions 15–17. Solve, using the five-step plan.

15. If 3 is subtracted from half a number, the result is 12. Find the number.

16. Barbara has 15 celebrity autographs. If she had 6 more, she would have as many as her friend, Sally. How many celebrity autographs does Sally have?

17. The number of Western High School freshmen studying French is 23 more than one-third the number studying Spanish. The total number of students enrolled in French is 52. How many students are enrolled in Spanish?

ANSWERS

1. _____ (4)

2. _____ (4)

3. _____ (4)

4. _____ (4)

5. _____ (4)

6. _____ (4)

7. _____ (4)

8. _____ (4)

9. _____ (5)

10. _____ (5)

11. _____ (5)

12. _____ (5)

13. _____ (4)

14. _____ (4)

15. _____ (5)

16. _____ (5)

17. _____ (6)

(continued)

Test 2—Test on Chapter 1 (continued)

Questions 18–20. Refer to the number line below. Write the coordinate of the point described.

```
 A   B   C   D   E   F   G
 ●   ●   ●   ●   ●   ●   ●
-3  -2  -1   0   1   2   3
```

18. The point halfway between D and G

19. The point two-thirds the distance from F to C

20. The point 2.5 units to the left of D

Questions 21–23. Simplify.

21. $-(-|2| \cdot |-5|)$ **22.** $-(|-23| + |15|)$

23. $|21| + |-19|$

Questions 24–25. Replace each $\underline{\quad ? \quad}$ with $<$, $=$, or $>$ to make a true statement.

24. $12 - 5 \underline{\quad ? \quad} 5 + |-12|$

25. $|5| - |-3| \underline{\quad ? \quad} |5| - |3|$

CHALLENGE *(Optional)* Gloria is four times as old as her brother, Bill. Three years ago, the sum of their ages was 14. How old is Gloria now?

ANSWERS	
18. _____	(3)
19. _____	(3)
20. _____	(3)
21. _____	(3)
22. _____	(3)
23. _____	(3)
24. _____	(3)
25. _____	(3)

CHALLENGE ANSWER

_____

ALGEBRA, Structure and Method, Book 1

Test 3—Test on Chapter 2 (Form A)

Directions. Write answers in the spaces provided. For each multiple-choice question, write the letter corresponding to the answer.

Questions 1–4. Simplify.

1. $14 - m + 6$

2. $-3 - [-(-6)]$

3. $20 \times 59 \times 5$

4. $-5 + [3 + (-3)]$

5. Solve the equation $-12 = 17 + b$.

Questions 6–7. Simplify.

6. $-2.3 - (-0.7) + 0.2$

7. $-\dfrac{1}{4} - \dfrac{5}{4} + 2$

8. During her summer vacation at camp, Donna lost 4 pounds the first week, gained $1\frac{1}{2}$ pounds the second week, gained $\frac{3}{4}$ pound the third week, and lost 3 pounds the fourth week. Did Donna gain or lose weight on her vacation, and how much?

Questions 9–16. Simplify.

9. $4 + (-1) - (-3)$

10. $2a - 3 + 5a - 10a + 8$

11. $5[7 + (-7)]$

12. $1.5n - 8 - 3.5n + 5$

13. $-7(a - 3b) + 9(-b + a)$

14. $2c - (1 - 3c) + (-c)$

15. $(-4)(-3)(-2)(-1)(0)$

16. $(-3)(-8)(-2)(10)$

Questions 17–20. Write an equation to represent the stated relationship among integers.

17. The sum of three consecutive integers is 15.

18. The smaller of two consecutive integers is four more than half of the greater.

19. A rectangle has an area of 110 cm². The lengths in centimeters of two adjacent sides are consecutive integers.

20. I am thinking of four consecutive integers. The sum of the second and fourth equals the third increased by 17.

ANSWERS	
1. _____	(3)
2. _____	(3)
3. _____	(3)
4. _____	(3)
5. _____	(3)
6. _____	(3)
7. _____	(3)
8. _____	(4)
9. _____	(4)
10. _____	(4)
11. _____	(4)
12. _____	(4)
13. _____	(4)
14. _____	(4)
15. _____	(4)
16. _____	(4)
17. _____	
_____	(4)
18. _____	(4)
19. _____	(4)
20. _____	
_____	(4)

(continued)

Test 3—Test on Chapter 2 (continued)

21. Which of the following is the reciprocal of -3?

    A. 3 **B.** $\dfrac{1}{3}$ **C.** $-\dfrac{1}{3}$ **D.** $\dfrac{-3}{1}$

22. Which of the following is an example of the distributive axiom of multiplication with respect to addition?

    A. $(a + b) + c = a + (b + c)$ **B.** $a + (-a) = 0$

    C. $a(b + c) = ab + ac$ **D.** $a(-1) = -a$

Questions 23–26. Simplify.

23. $(7c)\left(-\dfrac{1}{7}\right)$ **24.** $\dfrac{-4}{\frac{4}{9}}$

25. $\dfrac{24.5}{-5}$ **26.** $-35\left(\dfrac{1}{6}\right)\left(-\dfrac{1}{7}\right)$

27. Fahrenheit temperature readings taken at 8 A.M. each morning one week were $2°$, $-3°$, $-1°$, $4°$, $0°$, $-2°$, and $0°$. Find the average 8 A.M. temperature for that week.

28. Which *one* of the following is *not* true?

    A. The additive inverse of $-\dfrac{1}{3}$ is $\dfrac{1}{3}$.

    B. The reciprocal of 3 is -3.

    C. The multiplicative inverse of 3 is $\dfrac{1}{3}$.

    D. The reciprocal of 1 is 1.

ANSWERS

21. _____ (3)

22. _____ (3)

23. _____ (3)

24. _____ (3)

25. _____ (3)

26. _____ (3)

27. _____ (4)

28. _____ (5)

CHALLENGE ANSWER

_____

_____

_____

_____

CHALLENGE *(Optional)* What two axioms can be used to show that the following equation is true for any real value of a?

$$a + [a + (-a)] = a$$

ALGEBRA, Structure and Method, Book 1
Copyright © 1986 by Houghton Mifflin Company. All rights reserved. Printed in U.S.A.

Test 4—Test on Chapter 2 (Form B)

Directions. Write answers in the spaces provided. For each multiple-choice question, write the letter corresponding to the answer.

Questions 1–4. Simplify.

1. $7 - n + 5$

2. $-5 + [-(-1)]$

3. $50 \times 75 \times 2$

4. $-7 - [4 + (-4)]$

5. Solve the equation $-6 = n - 14$.

Questions 6–7. Simplify.

6. $-1.3 - (-2.0) + 0.3$

7. $4 - \dfrac{9}{5} + \dfrac{2}{5}$

8. One business week the dollar value of a stock changed as follows: Monday, down $1\frac{1}{8}$; Tuesday, down $\frac{3}{8}$; Wednesday, up $\frac{5}{8}$; Thursday, down $1\frac{3}{4}$; Friday, up $2\frac{1}{8}$. Find the stock's change in dollar value for the week.

Questions 9–16. Simplify.

9. $3 - (-2) + (-5)$

10. $4r - 7 + 3r + 9 - 8r$

11. $21[2 + (-2)]$

12. $3.2d - 5 - 4.5d + 3$

13. $3(p - 2q) - (5q - 2p)$

14. $-2a - (1 - 5a) + (-2a)$

15. $(-3)(-2)(-1)(0)(1)$

16. $(-6)(-3)(100)(-10)$

Questions 17–20. Write an equation to represent the stated relationship among integers.

17. The sum of two consecutive integers is 99.

18. The larger of two consecutive integers is eleven more than one-half the smaller.

19. The perimeter of a rectangle is 82 cm. The lengths in centimeters of two adjacent sides are consecutive integers.

20. I am thinking of three consecutive integers. Four times the third decreased by one-half the second is 4.

ANSWERS

1. _____ (3)
2. _____ (3)
3. _____ (3)
4. _____ (3)
5. _____ (3)
6. _____ (3)
7. _____ (3)
8. _____ (4)
9. _____ (4)
10. _____ (4)
11. _____ (4)
12. _____ (4)
13. _____ (4)
14. _____ (4)
15. _____ (4)
16. _____ (4)
17. _____ (4)
18. _____ (4)
19. _____
_____ (4)
20. _____
_____ (4)

(continued)

Test 4—Test on Chapter 2 *(continued)*

21. Which of the following is the reciprocal of -1?

    A. 0 **B.** 1 **C.** -1 **D.** $-(-1)$

22. Which of the following is an example of the axiom of opposites?

    A. $a + 0 = a$ **B.** $a + (-a) = 0$

    C. $a\left(\dfrac{1}{a}\right) = 1$ **D.** $-(-a) = a$

Questions 23–26. Simplify.

23. $\left(-\dfrac{1}{5}\right)(5b)$ **24.** $\dfrac{-5}{\dfrac{5}{8}}$

25. $\dfrac{-8}{\dfrac{1}{4}}$ **26.** $-24\left(-\dfrac{1}{5}\right)\left(\dfrac{1}{8}\right)$

27. A merchant's transactions resulted in the following: a gain of \$35, a gain of \$14, a loss of \$26, a gain of \$18, and a loss of \$9. Find the average gain or loss per transaction.

28. Which *one* of the following is *not* true?

    A. The reciprocal of 3 is $\dfrac{1}{3}$.

    B. The multiplicative inverse of -1 is -1.

    C. The additive inverse of $\dfrac{2}{3}$ is $\dfrac{3}{2}$.

    D. The additive inverse of -7 is 7.

ANSWERS

21. _____ (3)

22. _____ (3)

23. _____ (3)

24. _____ (3)

25. _____ (3)

26. _____ (3)

27. _____ (4)

28. _____ (5)

CHALLENGE ANSWERS

a. _____

   _____

b. _____

   _____

CHALLENGE *(Optional)* State the property or definition that justifies each of the following.

a. $-(a + b) = -a + (-b)$

b. $a - b = a + (-b)$

Test 5—Test on Chapter 3 (Form A)

Directions: Write answers in the spaces provided. For each matching question, write the letter corresponding to the answer.

Questions 1–12. Solve each equation. If the equation is an identity or if it has no root, state that fact.

1. $18y = 203 - 11y$

2. $7 = \dfrac{n}{2} - 1$

3. $360 + 36z = 30z$

4. $\dfrac{3w}{4} + 13 = 7$

5. $11 - \dfrac{n}{5} = |{-19}|$

6. $\dfrac{3x}{0.5} = 0.6$

7. $5(x + 1) = 4(x + 2)$

8. $39b = 171 + b$

9. $12\left(\dfrac{x}{3} - \dfrac{1}{2}\right) = 4x + 21$

10. $-20y = 221 + 6y$

11. $5(y + 2) = 6 + 3(2y - 1)$

12. $\dfrac{2}{5}(x + 1) + \dfrac{3}{5}(x + 1) = 14$

Questions 13–16. Solve each problem.

13. At its Grand Opening, the Guthrie Market distributed two different types of souvenirs. One type cost 20 cents each, and the other type cost 25 cents each. One thousand souvenirs were distributed in all. If the cost of these souvenirs was $220, how many of each type were distributed?

14. Find three consecutive integers such that five times the third integer equals twice the first integer plus seven more than the second integer.

15. The length of a rectangular playground exceeds twice its width by 25 meters. The perimeter of the playground is 650 meters. Find the dimensions of the playground.

16. Tina's father is 7 times as old as Tina. One year ago he was 9 times as old as she was. Find the present age of each.

ANSWERS

1. _____ (4)
2. _____ (4)
3. _____ (4)
4. _____ (4)
5. _____ (4)
6. _____ (4)
7. _____ (4)
8. _____ (4)
9. _____ (4)
10. _____ (4)
11. _____ (4)
12. _____ (4)
13. _____
    _____ (5)
14. _____ (5)
15. _____
    _____ (5)
16. _____
    _____ (5)

(continued)

Test 5—Test on Chapter 3 *(continued)*

Questions 17–20. Match each equation in Column I with the operation in Column II that you would use to solve the equation.

Column I

17. $\dfrac{x}{3} = 2$

18. $x - 3 = 7$

19. $x + 3 = 4$

20. $3x = 21$

Column II

A. Divide by 3.

B. Multiply by 3.

C. Add 3.

D. Subtract 3.

ANSWERS

17. _____ (4)

18. _____ (4)

19. _____ (4)

20. _____ (4)

21. _____ (4)

22. _____ (4)

23. _____ (4)

24. _____ (4)

CHALLENGE ANSWERS

_____

_____

_____

Questions 21–24. Match each statement in the following proof with the axiom or property that justifies the step. (*Hint:* You will not use all the axioms and properties.)

STATEMENTS	REASONS
$3x = -9$	Given
21. $\dfrac{1}{3}(3x) = \dfrac{1}{3}(-9)$	____?____
22. $\left(\dfrac{1}{3} \cdot 3\right)x = \dfrac{1}{3}(-9)$	____?____
23. $1x = \dfrac{1}{3}(-9)$	____?____
24. $x = \dfrac{1}{3}(-9)$	____?____
$x = -3$	Multiplication fact

A. Identity axiom
for multiplication

B. Associative axiom
for multiplication

C. Multiplication property
of equality

D. Axiom of reciprocals

E. Axiom of opposites

CHALLENGE *(Optional)* A health-food shop sells three grades of fiber products, grade A for $1.80 a pound, grade B for $1.30 a pound, and grade C for 65¢ a pound. The shopkeeper uses all three grades of fiber products to make 21 pounds of a mixture that will sell for $1 a pound. He uses twice as many pounds of grade C fiber as grade B fiber. How many pounds of each grade of fiber does he use?

ALGEBRA, Structure and Method, Book 1

Test 6—Test on Chapter 3 (Form B)

Directions: Write answers in the spaces provided. For each matching question, write the letter corresponding to the answer.

Questions 1–12. Solve each equation. If the equation is an identity or if it has no root, state that fact.

1. $\dfrac{2y}{3} + 7 = |-5|$

2. $\dfrac{5y}{0.2} = 0.3$

3. $3(8x - 2) = 3(4 + 2x)$

4. $-47w = 40 + 13w$

5. $\dfrac{4}{5}(a + 10) = a$

6. $106x = 540 + 34x$

7. $20 + \dfrac{7s}{2} = 15 + 3.5s + 5$

8. $5(y + 2) = 13 + 4(2y - 1)$

9. $15x = 144 - 9x$

10. $3(x - 5) = 2(x + 1) + x$

11. $714 + 38r = 21r$

12. $9 = \dfrac{x}{5} - 1$

Questions 13–16. Solve each problem.

13. Sherry is five times as old as her son. In 5 years she will be only three times as old as her son will be. How old is each now?

14. On the first day of school, the school bookstore sold 348 notebooks, some at 25¢ each and the rest at 38¢ each. The total amount of money paid for the notebooks was $100.91. How many of each kind were sold?

15. Three times the smaller of two consecutive even integers is four less than twice the larger. What are the two integers?

16. A rectangle measures 9 feet by 8 feet. Its area is three times the area of another rectangle 12 feet long. Find the width of the second rectangle.

ANSWERS

1. _____ (4)
2. _____ (4)
3. _____ (4)
4. _____ (4)
5. _____ (4)
6. _____ (4)
7. _____ (4)
8. _____ (4)
9. _____ (4)
10. _____ (4)
11. _____ (4)
12. _____ (4)
13. _____
   _____ (5)
14. _____
   _____ (5)
15. _____ (5)
16. _____ (5)

(continued)

Test 6—Test on Chapter 3 (continued)

Questions 17–20. Match each equation in Column I with the operation in Column II that you would use to solve the equation.

Column I

17. $\dfrac{x}{5} = 3$

18. $5x = 40$

19. $x - 5 = 0$

20. $x + 5 = 3$

Column II

A. Add 5.

B. Multiply by 5.

C. Subtract 5.

D. Divide by 5.

Questions 21–24. Match each statement in the following proof with the appropriate axiom or property that justifies the step. (You will not use all the axioms and properties.)

STATEMENTS	REASONS
$n + 5 = 7$	Given
21. $n + 5 + (-5) = 7 + (-5)$	___?___
22. $n + [5 + (-5)] = 7 + (-5)$	___?___
23. $n + 0 = 7 + (-5)$	___?___
24. $n = 7 + (-5)$	___?___
$n = 2$	Addition fact

A. Addition property of equality

B. Identity axiom for multiplication

C. Identity axiom for addition

D. Associative axiom for addition

E. Axiom of opposites

ANSWERS

17. _____ (4)

18. _____ (4)

19. _____ (4)

20. _____ (4)

21. _____ (4)

22. _____ (4)

23. _____ (4)

24. _____ (4)

CHALLENGE ANSWERS

_____

_____

_____

_____

CHALLENGE *(Optional)* Yoko paid $9.80 for stamps. She bought three times as many 22-cent stamps as 14-cent stamps, twice as many 2-cent stamps as 22-cent stamps, and the same number of 1-cent stamps as 2-cent stamps. How many stamps of each type did Yoko buy?

ALGEBRA, Structure and Method, Book 1
Copyright © 1986 by Houghton Mifflin Company. All rights reserved. Printed in U.S.A.

Test 7—Cumulative Test (Chapters 1–3)

Directions: Write answers in the spaces provided.

Questions 1–15. Simplify.

1. $-(-4) + (-6)$

2. $\dfrac{72 \div 8}{12}$

3. $39 \div (15 - 2)$

4. $-(2|-5|)$

5. $-4 + 7 + [-(-9)]$

6. $1 + 15.6 \div 12$

7. $15\frac{1}{2} + (-3\frac{1}{4}) + (-6\frac{7}{8})$

8. $72 \div 6 - 2 \times 3$

9. $|-4| + |-8|$

10. $\dfrac{18 \div 9 + 3 \times 4}{2(3 + 4)}$

11. $-[-(-7 + 9)]$

12. $-2(r + 3s) + 5(-r - s)$

13. $x + y - (x - y) - y$

14. $-[0.9 + (-5)]$

15. $-|-7| + |7|$

Questions 16–20. Evaluate each of the following expressions if $a = -2$, $b = 1$, $c = \dfrac{1}{3}$, and $d = 0$.

16. $-(|a| + c) + d$

17. $a(b - 3c)$

18. $\dfrac{-(a + d)}{c}$

19. $\dfrac{ab - d}{c}$

20. $ab + c - d$

Questions 21–25. Write the coordinate of the given point.

```
   A  B  C  D  E  F  G  H  I  J  K  L  M
  -6 -5 -4 -3 -2 -1  0  1  2  3  4  5  6
```

21. J **22.** D **23.** G **24.** M **25.** A

ANSWERS

1. _____ (1)
2. _____ (1)
3. _____ (1)
4. _____ (1)
5. _____ (1)
6. _____ (1)
7. _____ (1)
8. _____ (1)
9. _____ (1)
10. _____ (1)
11. _____ (1)
12. _____ (1)
13. _____ (1)
14. _____ (1)
15. _____ (1)
16. _____ (3)
17. _____ (3)
18. _____ (3)
19. _____ (3)
20. _____ (3)
21. _____ (1)
22. _____ (1)
23. _____ (1)
24. _____ (1)
25. _____ (1)

(continued)

Test 7—Cumulative Test (continued)

Questions 26–40. Solve. If the equation is an identity or has no solution, state that fact.

26. $|k| = 7$

27. $|x| + 3 = 0$

28. $y - |-3| = -1$

29. $\dfrac{z}{3} = -6$

30. $-12m + 8 = -13m$

31. $-5 + 8x - 3x = 40$

32. $\dfrac{t}{-5} = -9$

33. $2(x - 5) = 2(x + 3) - 16$

34. $5k - 3k = -6$

35. $9(2x + 8) = 20 - (x + 5)$

36. $7(3 - a) = a$

37. $6 + |x| = 4$

38. $7m + 5(3 - m) = 19$

39. $69 = 4(h + 5) - (h - 1)$

40. $7n + |5| + |-3| - n = |-8|$

Questions 41–44. Solve.

41. Find four consecutive even integers whose sum is 164.

42. Luanne bought 50 stamps, some costing 22 cents each, and the rest costing 14 cents each. She paid the postal clerk $10.04 for all the stamps. How many of each type of stamp did Luanne buy?

43. A rectangle has a perimeter of 34 cm. The lengths in centimeters of its adjacent sides are consecutive integers. Find the dimensions of the rectangle.

44. Two numbers differ by 5. Five times the lesser, diminished by two times the larger, is 11. Find the numbers.

ANSWERS

26. _____ (3)

27. _____ (3)

28. _____ (3)

29. _____ (3)

30. _____ (3)

31. _____ (3)

32. _____ (3)

33. _____ (3)

34. _____ (3)

35. _____ (3)

36. _____ (3)

37. _____ (3)

38. _____ (3)

39. _____ (3)

40. _____ (3)

41. _____

_____ (5)

42. _____

_____ (5)

43. _____ (5)

44. _____ (5)

ALGEBRA, Structure and Method, Book 1

Test 8—Test on Chapter 4 (Form A)

Directions: Write answers in the spaces provided.

Questions 1–3. Rewrite each expression in exponential form.

1. Five times the cube of y

2. The cube of the sum of r and 2

3. One-half the second power of g

Questions 4–5. **(a)** Add the polynomials. **(b)** Subtract the lower polynomial from the upper one.

4. $\begin{aligned} 5x^2 - 21x + 4 \\ -x^2 - 11x + 6 \end{aligned}$

5. $\begin{aligned} x^2 + 2x - 3 \\ 3x^2 - 2x - 8 \end{aligned}$

Questions 6–11. Simplify.

6. $2x^3 \cdot 5x^2$

7. $(x^2)(x^3)(x)$

8. $(-2a^2b^2)(5a)$

9. $(8m)(2mn)^3$

10. $-(3m^2n^3)^2$

11. $9n^3\left(\dfrac{1}{3}n\right)^4$

Questions 12–17. Multiply.

12. $-6(a^2 - 2a + 1)$

13. $(-2a)(a^2 - 3a)$

14. $(a - b)(a^2 + ab + b^2)$

15. $(a + b)(a^2 - ab + b^2)$

16. $(2x + 3)(5x + 1)$

17. $(3a - 5)^2$

Questions 18–21. Solve for the variable indicated.

18. $A = \dfrac{1}{2}(m + 22); \; m$

19. $P = 2b + 2h; \; b$

20. $3ax - 2 = 5ax - 1; \; x$

21. $A = \dfrac{1}{2}h(a + b); \; h$

ANSWERS

1. _____ (2)
2. _____ (2)
3. _____ (2)
4. a. _____ (2)
   b. _____ (2)
5. a. _____ (2)
   b. _____ (2)
6. _____ (3)
7. _____ (3)
8. _____ (3)
9. _____ (3)
10. _____ (3)
11. _____ (3)
12. _____ (3)
13. _____ (3)
14. _____ (3)
15. _____ (3)
16. _____ (3)
17. _____ (3)
18. _____ (5)
19. _____ (5)
20. _____ (5)
21. _____ (5)

(continued)

Test 8—Test on Chapter 4 *(continued)*

Questions 22–26. Solve each problem. If a problem has no solution, state that fact.

22. Two helicopters take off at the same time from the same airport and travel in opposite directions. The average speeds of the two craft are 350 km/h and 325 km/h respectively. In how many hours will the two helicopters be 2025 km apart?

23. Find four consecutive integers such that the sum of the third and fourth is 128.

24. Sally is five years older than Lynn. Five years ago Sally was twice as old as Lynn. How old is each now?

25. At 8 A.M. a freight train leaves River City and heads for Rockville. At the same time, a passenger train leaves Rockville and heads toward River City on parallel tracks. The passenger train averages 50 mph faster than the freight train. The two trains pass each other at noon. If River City and Rockville are 520 miles apart, what is the average speed of each train?

26. The length of a rectangle is 4 cm greater than its width. If the length and the width were both increased by 3 cm, the area of the rectangle would be increased by 93 cm². What are the dimensions of the original rectangle?

CHALLENGE *(Optional)* A ship must average 22 miles per hour to make its ten-hour run on schedule. During the first four hours, bad weather caused it to reduce its speed to 16 mph. What should be its speed for the rest of the trip to keep the ship on schedule?

ANSWERS

22. _____ (6)

23. _____ (6)

24. _____

_____ (6)

25. _____

_____ (6)

26. _____ (6)

CHALLENGE ANSWER

_____

ALGEBRA, Structure and Method, Book 1

Test 9—Test on Chapter 4 (Form B)

Directions: Write answers in the spaces provided.

Questions 1–3. Rewrite each expression in exponential form.

1. The square of the sum of t and 7

2. One-fourth of the fifth power of h

3. Eight times the square of z

Questions 4–5. (a) Add the polynomials. **(b)** Subtract the lower polynomial from the upper one.

4.	$7x^2 - 13x - 5$		5.	$x^2 + 8x + 10$
	$-2x^2 + 10x - 3$			$2x^2 - 8x + 10$

Questions 6–11. Simplify.

6. $(-x^2)(3x^3)$ 7. $(x^5)(x^3)(x)$ 8. $(-9a^3b^2)(3b)$

9. $(3y)(5xy^3)$ 10. $(-3mn^3)^2$ 11. $-(4x^2y)^2$

Questions 12–17. Multiply.

12. $-x(x^2 - 7x - 1)$ 13. $(2a^2 + 5a)(-a)$

14. $(m - 3)(m^2 + 3m + 9)$ 15. $(m + 3)(m^2 - 3m + 9)$

16. $(4x - 3)(5x - 1)$ 17. $(a - 3b)^2$

Questions 18–21. Solve for the variable indicated.

18. $H = 2r + 3m$; m 19. $W = \dfrac{11}{2}(h - 40)$; h

20. $5ab + 3 = 2ab - 1$; b 21. $P = 2(a + b)$; a

ANSWERS

1. _____ (2)
2. _____ (2)
3. _____ (2)
4. a. _____ (2)
   b. _____ (2)
5. a. _____ (2)
   b. _____ (2)
6. _____ (3)
7. _____ (3)
8. _____ (3)
9. _____ (3)
10. _____ (3)
11. _____ (3)
12. _____ (3)
13. _____ (3)
14. _____ (3)
15. _____ (3)
16. _____ (3)
17. _____ (3)
18. _____ (5)
19. _____ (5)
20. _____ (5)
21. _____ (5)

(continued)

Test 9—Test on Chapter 4 (continued)

Questions 22–26. Solve each problem. If a problem has no solution, state that fact.

22. Two jets leave Marble airport at 3 P.M., one traveling east and the other traveling west. The westbound jet averages 625 km/h, and the eastbound jet averages 825 km/h. At what time will the jets be 725 km apart?

23. Find three consecutive integers such that the sum of the first and third is 63.

24. Judy is five years younger than Rose. Five years ago Judy was half as old as Rose. How old is each now?

25. At noon Wally leaves Freeport and drives toward Center City. At the same time, Susan leaves Center City and drives toward Freeport along the same highway. Susan drives 10 mph faster than Wally. They pass each other at 3 P.M. If Freeport and Center City are 270 miles apart, what is the average speed of each driver?

26. The length of a rectangular piece of cardboard is 2 cm greater than its width. If the length and the width were each decreased by 1 cm, the area of the cardboard would be decreased by 27 cm². What are the dimensions of the original piece of cardboard?

ANSWERS

22. _____ (6)

23. _____ (6)

24. _____

_____ (6)

25. _____

_____ (6)

26. _____ (6)

CHALLENGE ANSWER

_____

CHALLENGE *(Optional)* Juan Rivera drove 80 miles into the country at an average rate of 55 mph. He then drove back on the same highway at an average rate of 45 mph. What was his average rate of speed for the entire round trip? (*Hint:* The answer is *not* 50 mph).

ALGEBRA, Structure and Method, Book 1
Copyright © 1986 by Houghton Mifflin Company. All rights reserved. Printed in U.S.A.

Test 10—Test on Chapter 5 (Form A)

Directions: Write answers in the spaces provided.

Questions 1–2. Give the prime factorization of each number.

1. 546

2. 392

Questions 3–4. Give the greatest common factor of each pair of numbers.

3. 85, 204

4. 80, 96

Questions 5–14. Perform each of the following multiplications or divisions and simplify your answers. Assume that no denominator equals zero.

5. $(a^2 - 8)(a^2 + 8)$

6. $\dfrac{-70de^7}{-7de}$

7. $(6x - 5)(7x - 8)$

8. $\dfrac{24n^3 - 12n^2 + 15n}{3n}$

9. $(5 + 3s)(5 - 3s)$

10. $(7x - 3)(5x + 2)$

11. $\dfrac{-5a^2b}{21(abc)^2}$

12. $(3x + 2a)^2$

13. $\dfrac{2n^4 - 3n^3 - 4n^2}{-n}$

14. $(c - 4d)^2$

Questions 15–32. Factor completely. If a polynomial cannot be factored, write "prime."

15. $-5ax^2 - 5ay^2$

16. $b^2 - 5b - 24$

17. $6y^3 + 3y^2 - 3y$

18. $2a^4 - 32$

19. $m^2 + 21m + 90$

20. $3x^2 - 5x + 2$

21. $dg + dm - fg - fm$

22. $y^2 + 26yz + 48z^2$

ANSWERS	
1. _____	(2)
2. _____	(2)
3. _____	(2)
4. _____	(2)
5. _____	(2)
6. _____	(2)
7. _____	(2)
8. _____	(2)
9. _____	(2)
10. _____	(2)
11. _____	(2)
12. _____	(2)
13. _____	(2)
14. _____	(2)
15. _____	(3)
16. _____	(3)
17. _____	(3)
18. _____	
_____	(3)
19. _____	(3)
20. _____	(3)
21. _____	(3)
22. _____	(3)

(continued)

Test 10—Test on Chapter 5 *(continued)*

Questions 15–32 (continued). Factor completely. If a polynomial cannot be factored, write "prime."

23. $49n^2 - 14n + 1$ **24.** $x^4 - 18x^2 + 81$

25. $x^2 + 4x - 10$ **26.** $25x^6 - x^4$

27. $b^2 + b - 132$ **28.** $6x^2 + 25x + 21$

29. $x^2 - 4xy + 4y^2 - 9$ **30.** $5 - 25y - 30y^2$

31. $2w^4 - 162$ **32.** $2n - n^2 - 1$

Questions 33–36. Solve.

33. $t^2 - 2t = 15$

34. $7m^2 = 168 + 35m$

35. $3x^2 = -12x$

36. I am thinking of two consecutive even integers. The sum of their squares is 100. Find the numbers.

CHALLENGE *(Optional)* The base of a triangle is 5 cm less than its height. Find the height and base if the area of the triangle is 63 cm^2.

ANSWERS

23. _____ (3)

24. _____ (3)

25. _____ (3)

26. _____ (3)

27. _____ (3)

28. _____ (3)

29. _____ (3)

30. _____ (3)

31. _____ (3)

32. _____ (3)

33. _____ (4)

34. _____ (4)

35. _____ (4)

36. _____

_____ (6)

CHALLENGE ANSWER

_____

ALGEBRA, Structure and Method, Book 1

Test 11—Test on Chapter 5 (Form B)

Directions: Write answers in the spaces provided.

Questions 1–2. Give the prime factorization of each number.

1. 252

2. 441

Questions 3–4. Give the greatest common factor of each pair of numbers.

3. 105, 126

4. 210, 245

Questions 5–14. Perform each of the following multiplications or divisions and simplify your answers. Assume that no denominator equals zero.

5. $(3y - 4)(4y - 6)$

6. $\dfrac{-4m^2n}{(4mnp)^3}$

7. $(y^2 + 5)(y^2 - 5)$

8. $(12w + 5)(5w - 2)$

9. $\dfrac{56rs^8}{-8rs^4}$

10. $(r - 8s)^2$

11. $(5x + 2y)^2$

12. $\dfrac{50r^3 + 10r^2 - 35r}{5r}$

13. $(6 + 5a)(6 - 5a)$

14. $\dfrac{8x^3 - 4x^2 - 2x}{-x}$

Questions 15–32. Factor completely. If a polynomial cannot be factored, write "prime."

15. $6v^3 + 26v^2 + 8v$

16. $n - n^5$

17. $3n^2 - 4n + 1$

18. $x^2 - 8x - 48$

19. $k^2 + k - 110$

20. $16s^2 - s^4$

21. $y^2 + 6y - 14$

22. $a^2 + 6ab + 9b^2 - 1$

ANSWERS

1. _____ (2)
2. _____ (2)
3. _____ (2)
4. _____ (2)
5. _____ (2)
6. _____ (2)
7. _____ (2)
8. _____ (2)
9. _____ (2)
10. _____ (2)
11. _____ (2)
12. _____ (2)
13. _____ (2)
14. _____ (2)
15. _____ (3)
16. _____ (3)
17. _____ (3)
18. _____ (3)
19. _____ (3)
20. _____ (3)
21. _____ (3)
22. _____ (3)

(continued)

Test 11—Test on Chapter 5 *(continued)*

Questions 15–32 (continued). Factor completely. If a polynomial cannot be factored, write "prime."

23. $r^2 + 33r + 90$

24. $rs - rt - ks + kt$

25. $-rt^3 - r^3t$

26. $14x^2 + 33x + 10$

27. $3 - 21y - 24y^2$

28. $a^4 - 8a^3 + 16a^2$

29. $3m^4 - 243$

30. $4b - 4b^2 - 1$

31. $x^2 + 14xy + 24y^2$

32. $25x^2 - 10x + 4$

Questions 33–36. Solve.

33. $s^2 - 3s = 18$

34. $6n^2 = 15n$

35. $8x^2 = 216 + 48x$

36. I am thinking of two consecutive odd integers. The sum of their squares is 202. Find the numbers.

CHALLENGE *(Optional)* The base of a triangle is 9 cm greater than its height. Find the base and height if the area of the triangle is 68 cm^2.

ANSWERS

23. _____ (3)

24. _____ (3)

25. _____ (3)

26. _____ (3)

27. _____ (3)

28. _____ (3)

29. _____ (3)

30. _____ (3)

31. _____ (3)

32. _____ (3)

33. _____ (4)

34. _____ (4)

35. _____ (4)

36. _____

_____ (6)

CHALLENGE ANSWER

_____

ALGEBRA, Structure and Method, Book 1

Test 12—Test on Chapter 6 (Form A)

Directions: Write answers in the spaces provided.

Questions 1–4. (a) Express in simplest form. (b) Give any restrictions on the variable.

1. $\dfrac{x^2 - 2x - 8}{x^2 - x - 6}$

2. $\dfrac{5c^2 - 45c + 90}{180 - 5c^2}$

3. $\dfrac{3x - 21}{42 - 6x}$

4. $\dfrac{6a^2 - 54}{2a^2 + 8a + 6}$

Questions 5–8. Express in simplest form.

5. $\dfrac{3}{5} \div \dfrac{5}{3}$

6. $(7x^3)^2 \cdot \dfrac{x}{2} \cdot \dfrac{x}{8}$

7. $\dfrac{a^2 b}{c} \div ab^2$

8. $\dfrac{2r^2 s^2}{9t^2 u^2} \cdot \dfrac{45tu}{14rs}$

Questions 9–10. Express each group of fractions with their LCD.

9. $\dfrac{2h + 1}{4}, \dfrac{h - 3}{6}$

10. $\dfrac{2a + 3b}{3a^2 b}, \dfrac{a + 2b}{4ab^2}, \dfrac{1}{6ab}$

Questions 11–16. Simplify.

11. $\dfrac{x^2}{x - 5} \cdot \dfrac{5 - x}{x^2}$

12. $\dfrac{y^2 - 2y + 1}{3x^2} \cdot \dfrac{x}{y - 1}$

13. $a + \dfrac{2}{a + 1} + 6$

14. $\dfrac{x^2 - x - 2}{x} \div \dfrac{x^2 - 4}{2x}$

15. $\dfrac{6m - 13}{m^2 - 5m + 6} - \dfrac{5}{m - 3}$

16. $\dfrac{x^2 - 3x - 10}{x^2 - x - 6} \div \dfrac{x^2 - 4x - 5}{x^2 - 2x - 3}$

ANSWERS	
1. a. _____	(3)
b. _____	(1)
2. a. _____	(3)
b. _____	(1)
3. a. _____	(3)
b. _____	(1)
4. a. _____	(3)
b. _____	(1)
5. _____	(4)
6. _____	(4)
7. _____	(4)
8. _____	(4)
9. _____	
_____	(4)
10. _____	
_____	
_____	(4)
11. _____	(5)
12. _____	(5)
13. _____	(5)
14. _____	(5)
15. _____	(5)
16. _____	(5)

(continued)

DATE   SCORE

Test 12—Test on Chapter 6 *(continued)*

Questions 17–20. Write each expression as a fraction in simplest form.

17. $\dfrac{a}{b} + 4$

18. $1 - \dfrac{3}{x + 1}$

19. $\dfrac{3}{x - 3} + \dfrac{x}{3 - x} + 1$

20. $\dfrac{5}{n} + 3 - \dfrac{n}{5}$

Questions 21–22. Divide. Write your answer as a polynomial or mixed expression.

21. $\dfrac{56 - 15x + x^2}{x - 7}$

22. $\dfrac{x^3 + x^2 - 11x + 5}{x + 4}$

CHALLENGE *(Optional)* Simplify the complex fraction $\dfrac{\dfrac{2}{a - 1} + \dfrac{a - 1}{a + 1}}{1 + \dfrac{a + 1}{a - 1}}$.

ANSWERS

17. _____ (5)

18. _____ (5)

19. _____ (5)

20. _____ (5)

21. _____ (5)

22. _____

_____ (5)

CHALLENGE ANSWER

_____

ALGEBRA, Structure and Method, Book 1
Copyright © 1986 by Houghton Mifflin Company. All rights reserved. Printed in U.S.A.

Test 13—Test on Chapter 6 (Form B)

Directions: Write answers in the spaces provided.

Questions 1–4. (a) Express in simplest form. **(b)** Give any restrictions on the variable.

1. $\dfrac{x^2 - 10x + 21}{x^2 - 4x - 21}$

2. $\dfrac{6c^2 - 15c - 9}{27 - 3c^2}$

3. $\dfrac{5x - 20}{24 - 6x}$

4. $\dfrac{3a^2 - 48}{a^2 + 8a + 16}$

Questions 5–8. Express in simplest form.

5. $\dfrac{2}{3} \div \dfrac{3}{2}$

6. $(3x^2)^2 \cdot \dfrac{1}{x} \cdot \dfrac{x}{3}$

7. $\dfrac{a^3 b^2}{c} \div ab^3$

8. $\dfrac{6r^3 t^2}{5rt^3} \cdot \dfrac{10rt^2}{r^2 t}$

Questions 9–10. Express each group of fractions with their LCD.

9. $\dfrac{3m + n}{5}, \dfrac{2n}{3}$

10. $\dfrac{a - b}{2a^2 b}, \dfrac{a}{ab}, \dfrac{b}{2a}$

Questions 11–16. Simplify.

11. $\dfrac{x^5}{x - 3} \cdot \dfrac{3 - x}{x^4}$

12. $\dfrac{y^2 - 6y + 5}{x} \cdot \dfrac{x^3}{y - 5}$

13. $b + \dfrac{1}{b + 1} + 1$

14. $\dfrac{x^2 - 2x - 3}{x} \div \dfrac{x^2 + 2x + 1}{x}$

15. $\dfrac{2n + 3}{n^2 - 1} - \dfrac{1}{n - 1}$

16. $\dfrac{n^2 + 4n - 5}{n^2 - 4n + 3} \div \dfrac{n^2 + 3n - 10}{n^2 - 5n + 6}$

ANSWERS

1. a. _____ (3)
   b. _____ (1)
2. a. _____ (3)
   b. _____ (1)
3. a. _____ (3)
   b. _____ (1)
4. a. _____ (3)
   b. _____ (1)
5. _____ (4)
6. _____ (4)
7. _____ (4)
8. _____ (4)
9. _____ (4)
10. _____
    _____ (4)
11. _____ (5)
12. _____ (5)
13. _____ (5)
14. _____ (5)
15. _____ (5)
16. _____ (5)

(continued)

Test 13—Test on Chapter 6   (continued)

Questions 17–20. Write each expression as a fraction in simplest form.

17. $\dfrac{m}{n} - 3$

18. $2 - \dfrac{5}{x - 3}$

19. $\dfrac{1}{x - 5} + \dfrac{2x}{5 - x} - 1$

20. $6 + \dfrac{3}{a} - \dfrac{a}{3}$

Questions 21–22. Divide. Write your answer as a polynomial or mixed expression.

21. $\dfrac{4x^2 - 30x + 14}{x - 7}$

22. $\dfrac{2x^3 + 2x^2 - 9x + 11}{x + 3}$

CHALLENGE *(Optional)* Simplify the complex fraction $\dfrac{1 + \dfrac{a + 3}{a - 3}}{1 + \dfrac{a - 3}{a + 3}}$.

ANSWERS

17. _____ (5)

18. _____ (5)

19. _____ (5)

20. _____ (5)

21. _____ (5)

22. _____

_____ (5)

CHALLENGE ANSWER

_____

Test 14—Cumulative Test (Chapters 4–6)

Directions: Write answers in the spaces provided.

Questions 1–20. Perform the indicated operations. Express the answers in simplest form. Assume that no denominator is zero.

1. $-x^2(5x^2 - x + 2)$

2. $(m + 3n)(m + 3n)$

3. $(2t^4 - t^2 + t - 1) + (t^5 - t^3 + 3 + 2t)$

4. $\dfrac{7c^3 + 14c}{7c}$

5. $\dfrac{6a - 3b}{4a^2 - b^2} \cdot \dfrac{2a + b}{3}$

6. $-3x(4x^3y^2)(-y^4x^2)$

7. $(15x^2 - 3x + 9) - (2x^2 + x - 3)$

8. $\dfrac{-60m^3n^3 + 36m^2n^2 - 6mn}{-6mn}$

9. $(z - 7) + (3z - 5) + (9z + 15)$

10. $\dfrac{c^2 + 4cd + 4d^2}{c^2 - 4d^2}$

11. $(-r)(-6r)^3$

12. $(x + 9)^2$

13. $(4x^2 - 7) - (5x^2 - 3x - 8)$

14. $5rs^2(3 + 4r^5s - r^3s^4 - 7rs^7)$

15. $(-7a^2)(5b)(-2b) + (4ab)(-2ab)$

16. $\dfrac{x}{x^2 - 25} - \dfrac{1}{2x + 10}$

17. $\dfrac{x^4 - y^4}{3x + 3y} \div \dfrac{2x^2 + 2y^2}{6}$

18. $\dfrac{3}{z^2 - 25} - \dfrac{1}{5 + z} - \dfrac{z + 1}{5 - z}$

19. $\dfrac{1}{a + b} + \dfrac{a}{a^2 - b^2}$

20. $\dfrac{3x - 1}{3x^2} \div \dfrac{3x + 1}{3x} \cdot \dfrac{9x^2 + 6x + 1}{9x^2 - 1}$

ANSWERS

1. _____ (2)
2. _____ (2)
3. _____

   _____ (2)
4. _____ (2)
5. _____ (2)
6. _____ (2)
7. _____ (2)
8. _____ (2)
9. _____ (2)
10. _____ (2)
11. _____ (2)
12. _____ (2)
13. _____ (2)
14. _____

    _____ (2)
15. _____ (2)
16. _____ (2)
17. _____ (2)
18. _____ (2)
19. _____ (2)
20. _____ (2)

(continued)

Test 14—Cumulative Test (continued)

Questions 21–28. Factor completely. If the polynomial cannot be factored, write "prime."

21. $a^2 + 3a - 40$

22. $12x^3 - 8x^2 - 20x$

23. $m^2 + 16n^4$

24. $x^2 + 20x + 51$

25. $az^2 - 12awz + 36aw^2$

26. $5r^2t - 10rt + 5rt^2$

27. $16r^2 + 40rt + 25t^2$

28. $3x^2 + 20x - 7$

Questions 29–37. Solve.

29. $x^2 = 108 + 3x$

30. $y^4 - 10y^2 + 9 = 0$

31. $6s^2 = s$

32. $25y^2 - 100 = 0$

33. $3k^2 + 10 = 17k$

34. $n^3 - 6n^2 - 40n = 0$

35. Find two numbers whose sum is 17 and whose squares total 145.

36. A rectangle is 5 feet longer than it is wide. The area of the rectangle is 66 ft². Find its dimensions.

37. An automobile travels 280 km at a certain speed. If the speed had been 5 km/h faster, the trip would have been made in 1 hour less time. Find the original speed of the automobile.

ANSWERS

21. _____ (3)
22. _____ (3)
23. _____ (3)
24. _____ (3)
25. _____ (3)
26. _____ (3)
27. _____ (3)
28. _____ (3)
29. _____ (4)
30. _____ (4)
31. _____ (4)
32. _____ (4)
33. _____ (4)
34. _____ (4)
35. _____ (4)
36. _____ (4)
37. _____ (4)

ALGEBRA, Structure and Method, Book 1
Copyright © 1986 by Houghton Mifflin Company. All rights reserved. Printed in U.S.A.

Test 15—Cumulative Test (Chapters 1–6)

Directions: Write answers in the spaces provided.

Questions 1–10. Classify each statement as true or false. Assume that all variables represent real numbers. If a statement involves variables, decide whether it is true for all real numbers.

1. If $a = b$, then $ac = bc$.

2. $a - b = b - a$

3. $a + (-a) = 1$

4. The reciprocal of 0 is 0.

5. The opposite of 1 is -1.

6. If $a < 0$, $|a| = -a$.

7. $a^2 + b^2 = (a + b)(a + b)$.

8. $a + a + a = a^3$

9. The reciprocal of 1 is -1.

10. $-|-(-1)| = -1$

Questions 11–13. Evaluate if $m = -2$, $n = -1$, $p = 3$, $r = -6$, and $t = 10$.

11. $\dfrac{(mp)^2 - r^2}{t^2}$

12. $\left(\dfrac{r}{m}\right)^3 - \dfrac{p^3}{3}$

13. $\dfrac{n^8 + (r - 1)^2}{(p + 2)^2}$

Questions 14–21. Simplify. Assume that no denominator is zero.

14. $(-5x)^2(2y^2x)^3$

15. $3.3 + 3(6)(0.5)$

16. $(2m - n)(n + 2m)$

17. $[8a + 5(3 - a)] - 17$

18. $\dfrac{64r^2 - 1}{64r^2 + 16r + 1} \cdot \dfrac{8r + 1}{16r - 2}$

19. $(-2m + 6n)^2$

20. $\dfrac{-48d^4h^3k^2}{-3d^4hk^4}$

21. $\dfrac{5c^2 - 5cd}{cd + d^2} \div \dfrac{d^3 - dc^2}{cd^2}$

ANSWERS

1. _____ (1)
2. _____ (1)
3. _____ (1)
4. _____ (1)
5. _____ (1)
6. _____ (1)
7. _____ (1)
8. _____ (1)
9. _____ (1)
10. _____ (1)
11. _____ (2)
12. _____ (2)
13. _____ (2)
14. _____ (2)
15. _____ (2)
16. _____ (2)
17. _____ (2)
18. _____ (2)
19. _____ (2)
20. _____ (2)
21. _____ (2)

(continued)

Test 15—Cumulative Test (continued)

Questions 22–27. Simplify. Assume that no denominator is zero.

22. $(2n - 9)(3n + 4)$

23. $-3x^2y(5 - 2xy^4 + 3x^2y^3 - y^5)$

24. $\dfrac{2x^3 + 20x^2 + 50x}{4x^3 + 100x}$

25. $(22n - k) - (13n - k)$

26. $\dfrac{4}{x - 2} + 1$

27. $\dfrac{2}{x - 1} - \dfrac{3}{1 + x} + \dfrac{x - 5}{x^2 - 1}$

Questions 28–33. Factor each polynomial completely.

28. $x^4 - y^4$

29. $y^2 + 10y + 25$

30. $x^2 + xy - 6y^2$

31. $4x^2 - 4x + 1$

32. $x^2 - 18x + 81$

33. $6a^2 - ab - b^2$

Questions 34–46. Solve. If the equation is an identity or has no solution, state that fact.

34. $7m + 5(3 - m) = 19$

35. $-12m + 8 = -13m$

36. $2w - 4(w + 2) = 5(w + 4)$

37. $y - 8 = -12$

38. $-2 = -2 + 5k$

39. $\dfrac{t}{-5} = -9$

40. $6 + |x| = 4$

41. $5k - 3k = -6$

ANSWERS

22. _____ (2)

23. _____

_____ (2)

24. _____ (2)

25. _____ (2)

26. _____ (2)

27. _____ (2)

28. _____ (2)

29. _____ (2)

30. _____ (2)

31. _____ (2)

32. _____ (2)

33. _____ (2)

34. _____ (2)

35. _____ (2)

36. _____ (2)

37. _____ (2)

38. _____ (2)

39. _____ (2)

40. _____ (2)

41. _____ (2)

(continued)

ALGEBRA, Structure and Method, Book 1

Test 15—Cumulative Test (continued)

Questions 34–46 (continued). Solve. If the equation is an identity or has no solution, state that fact.

42. $-3z = 15$

43. $4(3n + 2) = 6(3 - n) + 8$

44. $x^2 + 8x = 0$

45. $x^2 + 14x + 45 = 0$

46. $8y + y^2 + 10 = -5$

Questions 47–52. Solve.

47. Anton has 52 coins, some of them quarters and the rest dimes. The value of the coins is $10.00. How many coins of each type does he have?

48. Mike Swann is twice as old as his youngest daughter. In 8 years, Mike's age will be three times as great as his daughter's age was six years ago. What are the present ages of Mike and his daughter?

49. Alice cycles to Carla's house at 12 mph and returns by car at 36 mph. If the round trip is 1 hour, how far from Carla does Alice live?

50. Find four consecutive whole numbers such that the sum of the squares of the first and third is 2 less than 6 times the fourth.

51. Find two numbers whose sum is 12 and whose squares total 104.

52. The length of a rectangle is four times its width. If the area of the rectangle is 36 cm^2, find the dimensions of the rectangle.

ANSWERS

42. _____ (2)

43. _____ (2)

44. _____ (2)

45. _____ (2)

46. _____ (2)

47. _____

_____ (3)

48. _____

_____ (3)

49. _____ (3)

50. _____ (3)

51. _____ (3)

52. _____ (3)

Test 16—Test on Chapter 7 (Form A)

Directions: Write answers in the spaces provided.

Questions 1–5. Write each ratio in simplest form.

1. 5 cm:3 m

2. 375 g:1 kg

3. 13 wk:2 yr

4. The ratio of wins to losses in 15 games with 8 wins and no ties

5. The ratio of x to y determined by the equation $14x = 10y$

Questions 6–13. Solve and check. If an equation has no solution, write "no solution."

6. $\dfrac{17}{m} = \dfrac{34}{5}$

7. $\dfrac{3n - 5}{2} - \dfrac{n}{3} = 8$

8. $\dfrac{y + 5}{2y} - \dfrac{7}{3y} = \dfrac{5}{12}$

9. $\dfrac{2x - 10}{x - 5} = 3$

10. $\dfrac{v - 1}{v + 3} = \dfrac{v + 3}{v}$

11. $\dfrac{n + 3}{2} = \dfrac{n - 8}{5} + 1$

12. $\dfrac{z}{z - 3} = \dfrac{7}{4}$

13. $\dfrac{2x}{x + 2} - 2 = \dfrac{x - 8}{x - 2}$

ANSWERS	
1. _____	(3)
2. _____	(3)
3. _____	(3)
4. _____	(3)
5. _____	(4)
6. _____	(4)
7. _____	(4)
8. _____	(4)
9. _____	(4)
10. _____	(4)
11. _____	(4)
12. _____	(4)
13. _____	(4)

(continued)

ALGEBRA, Structure and Method, Book 1

Test 16—Test on Chapter 7 (continued)

Questions 14–19. Solve.

14. Two printing presses can turn out one day's newspapers in 6 hours. The faster press can do the job, operating alone, in 10 hours. How long would it take the slower press, operating alone, to do the job?

15. Two numbers are in the ratio 7:8, and their sum is 135. What are the numbers?

16. Kristen spent $24 for a video tape. This was 30% of the money she received as birthday gifts. How much gift money did she receive?

17. Sula bought a camera on sale for $19.50. This price was 60% of the regular price. What was the regular price?

18. How much water must be added to a barrel containing 48 gallons of a 10% salt solution to obtain a 6% salt solution?

19. Carlos went shopping with $52. He spent $39. What percent of the $52 did he spend?

Questions 20–23. Simplify. Give answers in terms of positive exponents.

20. $(-2x^0y^{-4})^{-2}$

21. $5^6 \cdot 5^{-3}$

22. $\dfrac{10^{-4}}{10^{-3}}$

23. $(6a^{-2}b^3c)^{-3}$

24. Rewrite 3.75×10^5 without using scientific notation.

25. Rewrite 0.00000000048 using scientific notation.

CHALLENGE *(Optional)* Working together, a man and his two sons assembled a set of electric trains in 12 minutes. Working alone, it would have taken the man 10 minutes less than it would have taken either son working alone. How long would it have taken the two sons, working together without their father, to assemble the set of trains?

ANSWERS	
14. _____	(6)
15. _____	(6)
16. _____	(6)
17. _____	(6)
18. _____	(6)
19. _____	(6)
20. _____	(3)
21. _____	(3)
22. _____	(3)
23. _____	(3)
24. _____	(2)
25. _____	(2)

CHALLENGE ANSWER

_____

Test 17—Test on Chapter 7 (Form B)

Directions: Write answers in the spaces provided.

Questions 1–5. State each ratio in simplest form.

1. 50 min : 1 h

2. 1200 g : 2 kg

3. 30 days : 12 weeks

4. The ratio of boys to girls in a school with 1500 students, 500 of whom are boys

5. The ratio of a to b determined by the equation $2a = 6b$

Questions 6–13. Solve and check. If an equation has no solution, write "no solution."

6. $\dfrac{w - 4}{w} = \dfrac{5}{9}$

7. $\dfrac{x + 1}{x} = \dfrac{x + 2}{x - 1}$

8. $\dfrac{n}{21} = \dfrac{3}{63}$

9. $\dfrac{3t}{2} + \dfrac{8 - 4t}{7} = 3$

10. $\dfrac{9z - 3}{3z - 1} = 5$

11. $\dfrac{y}{y - 16} = \dfrac{5}{3}$

12. $\dfrac{n - 3}{4} = \dfrac{2n - 5}{5} + 1$

13. $\dfrac{4z}{z - 3} - 3 = \dfrac{3z - 1}{z + 3}$

Questions 14–19. Solve.

14. How much water must be added to 3 quarts of a 30% acid solution to form a 20% acid solution?

15. Adela earned $12,500 last year and donated 5% of her salary to charity. How much money did she donate to charity?

ANSWERS	
1. _____	(3)
2. _____	(3)
3. _____	(3)
4. _____	(3)
5. _____	(4)
6. _____	(4)
7. _____	(4)
8. _____	(4)
9. _____	(4)
10. _____	(4)
11. _____	(4)
12. _____	(4)
13. _____	(4)
14. _____	(6)
15. _____	(6)

(continued)

Test 17—Test on Chapter 7 *(continued)*

16. Gina and Cal can spray an orchard in 8 hours. Gina, working alone, would take 12 hours to do the job. How long would it take Cal working alone?

17. On the sale of a used car, Bert received a commission of $247.50. If he works for a 15% commission, what was the price of the car he sold?

18. Two numbers are in the ratio of 5:11. The sum of the two numbers is 64. Find the numbers.

19. Linda went food shopping with $35 in her purse. She spent $28. What percent of the $35 did she spend?

Questions 20–23. Simplify. Give answers in terms of positive exponents.

20. $(8x^{-4}y^5z^2)^{-2}$

21. $\dfrac{12^{-5}}{12^{-4}}$

22. $(3^{-2})^{-2}$

23. $8^{-2} \cdot 8^4$

24. Rewrite 1.79×10^4 without using scientific notation.

25. Rewrite 186,000,000 using scientific notation.

CHALLENGE *(Optional)* Working together, three men can paint a barn in 6 hours. If each man worked alone, the first man would take twice as long as the second, and the second would take 6 hours longer than the third. How many hours would it take the slowest man, working alone, to paint the barn?

ANSWERS	
16. _____	(6)
17. _____	(6)
18. _____	(6)
19. _____	(6)
20. _____	(3)
21. _____	(3)
22. _____	(3)
23. _____	(3)
24. _____	(2)
25. _____	(2)

CHALLENGE ANSWER

_____

Test 18—Test on Chapter 8 (Form A)

Directions: Write answers in the spaces provided.

Questions 1–2. State whether each ordered pair is a solution of the equation $2x - 3y = 8$.

1. (19, 10)

2. (5, −6)

Questions 3–4. Solve each equation for y in terms of x.

3. $6x + 2y = 3$

4. $7x - 2y = -2$

Questions 5–8. Refer to the diagram. Name the point(s) described.

5. The x-coordinate equals the y-coordinate.

6. The x-coordinate is zero.

7. The y-coordinate is zero.

8. The x-coordinate is the opposite of the y-coordinate.

9. Graph the equation $y = \dfrac{1}{2}x$.

Use the diagram shown.

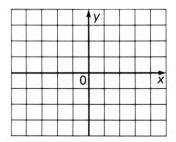

10. Solve the following system by the graphic method. Use the diagram shown.

$$x - y = -1$$
$$x + y = 3$$

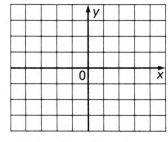

ANSWERS

1. _____ (3)

2. _____ (3)

3. _____ (3)

4. _____ (3)

5. _____ (3)

6. _____ (3)

7. _____ (3)

8. _____ (3)

9. *See diagram.* (5)

10. *See diagram.* (10)

(continued)

Test 18—Test on Chapter 8 (continued)

11. Use the addition-or-subtraction method to solve the system:
$5m - 3n = 19$
$2m + 3n = -5$

12. Use the substitution method to solve the system: $2x + y = 7$
$y = 5x$

13. Use multiplication with the addition-or-subtraction method to solve the system: $4d - 5c = -22$
$c - 2d = 5$

Questions 14–17. Solve by using a system of equations in two variables.

14. The ratio of boys to girls in Jill's homeroom is $4:3$. There would be an equal number of boys and girls if there were 3 more girls and 2 fewer boys. How many boys and girls are in the homeroom?

15. The sum of the digits of a two-digit number is 12. If 36 is added to the number, the new number obtained is the original number with its digits interchanged. Find the original number.

16. It took 40 minutes for Dale and Tami to paddle 6 miles downstream on White River. It then took 3 hours for them to return the same distance. They paddled at the same average rate, both down and back. What was the speed of the river's current?

17. The denominator of a fraction is 5 more than the numerator. If 1 is subtracted from the numerator, the resulting fraction is equal to $\dfrac{1}{3}$. Find the original fraction.

CHALLENGE *(Optional)* The numerator of a fraction consists of two digits with a sum of 12. The denominator of the fraction is formed by reversing the digits in the numerator. If 11 is added to the numerator, and 7 is added to the denominator, the resulting fraction has a value of $\dfrac{1}{2}$. Find the original fraction.

ANSWERS

11. _____ (7)

12. _____ (7)

13. _____ (7)

14. _____ (10)

15. _____ (10)

16. _____ (10)

17. _____ (10)

CHALLENGE ANSWER

_____

Test 19—Test on Chapter 8 (Form B)

Directions: Write answers in the spaces provided.

Questions 1–2. State whether each ordered pair is a solution of the equation
$-3x + 5y = -8$.

1. $(16, 8)$

2. $(-6, -2)$

Questions 3–4. Solve each equation for y in terms of x.

3. $7x - y = 0$

4. $5x - 2y = 8$

Questions 5–8. Refer to the diagram. Name the point(s) described.

5. The x-coordinate is negative.

6. The y-coordinate is negative.

7. The x-coordinate equals the y-coordinate.

8. The x-coordinate is the opposite of the y-coordinate.

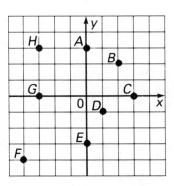

9. Graph the equation $3y + 2x - 6 = 0$. Use the diagram shown.

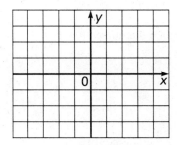

10. Solve the following system by the graphic method. Use the diagram shown.

$$3x - 4y = -9$$
$$y = 3x$$

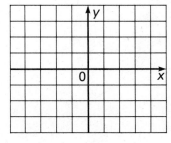

ANSWERS	
1. _____	(3)
2. _____	(3)
3. _____	(3)
4. _____	(3)
5. _____	(3)
6. _____	(3)
7. _____	(3)
8. _____	(3)
9. *See diagram.*	(5)
10. *See diagram.*	(10)

(continued)

ALGEBRA, Structure and Method, Book 1

Test 19—Test on Chapter 8 *(continued)*

11. Use the addition-or-subtraction method to solve the
system: $4w - 5z = 10$
$2w + 5z = -10$

12. Use the substitution method to solve the system: $x + 2y = 5$
$x = 3y$

13. Use multiplication with the addition-or-subtraction method to solve
the system: $5p - 3w = 6$
$7w + p = -52$

Questions 14–17. Solve by using a system of equations in two variables.

14. The ratio of boys to girls in a school's graduating class is $2:3$. There
would be an equal number of boys and girls if there were 30 more boys
and 30 fewer girls. How many boys and how many girls are there in the
graduating class?

15. The sum of the digits of a two-digit number is 14. If 36 is subtracted
from the number, the resulting number is the original number with its
digits interchanged. Find the original number.

16. Pat biked 1 mile in 3 minutes with the wind at her back, and then she
returned in 4 minutes riding against the wind. What was the speed of
the wind?

17. A fraction has a value of $\dfrac{3}{4}$. If 7 is added to the numerator, the resulting fraction is equal to the reciprocal of the original fraction. Find the
original fraction.

CHALLENGE *(Optional)* A fraction has the value of $\dfrac{4}{7}$. The two digits in
the numerator are interchanged in the denominator. If 11 is added to the
numerator, and 22 is subtracted from the denominator, the resulting fraction
is the reciprocal of the original fraction. Find the original fraction.

ANSWERS

11. _____ (7)

12. _____ (7)

13. _____ (7)

14. _____ (10)

15. _____ (10)

16. _____ (10)

17. _____ (10)

CHALLENGE ANSWER

_____

Test 20—Test on Chapter 9 (Form A)

Directions: Write answers in the spaces provided.

Questions 1–4. Find **(a)** the slope and **(b)** the y-intercept of the line determined by the given condition.

1. Its equation is $y - 3x = 4$.

2. It contains the points $(2, 4)$ and $(3, 5)$.

3. Its equation is $2x - 5y = 0$.

4. It passes through the points $(-1, -6)$ and $(1, -6)$.

Questions 5–8. Write in standard form the equation of the line determined by the given condition.

5. It has no slope and it passes through $(3, 2)$.

6. It has zero slope and it passes through the origin.

7. It has slope $\dfrac{1}{3}$ and y-intercept 2.

8. It contains the points $(0, 1)$ and $(2, 0)$.

Questions 9–10. **(a)** Change each equation to slope-intercept form. **(b)** Draw the graph using only the slope and y-intercept.

9. $3x + 4y = 12$ 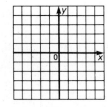   **10.** $2x + y = 4$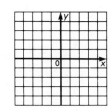

Questions 11–14. Determine whether or not each is a function.

11. $y = -x^2$ **12.** $\{(1, 0), (2, 0), (3, 0)\}$

13. $y = x - 3$ **14.** $\{(0, 1), (0, 2), (0, 3)\}$

ANSWERS

1. a. _____ (2)

   b. _____ (2)

2. a. _____ (2)

   b. _____ (2)

3. a. _____ (2)

   b. _____ (2)

4. a. _____ (2)

   b. _____ (2)

5. _____ (4)

6. _____ (4)

7. _____ (4)

8. _____ (4)

9. a. _____ (4)

   b. *See diagram.* (4)

10. a. _____ (4)

    b. *See diagram.* (4)

11. _____ (3)

12. _____ (3)

13. _____ (3)

14. _____ (3)

(continued)

ALGEBRA, Structure and Method, Book 1
Copyright © 1986 by Houghton Mifflin Company. All rights reserved. Printed in U.S.A.

Test 20—Test on Chapter 9 *(continued)*

Questions 15–17. {(1, 8), (2, 3), (3, 12), (4, 9), (5, 10), (6, 5)} describes a function.

15. State the domain.

16. State the range.

17. Make a broken-line graph for the function. Use the diagram shown.

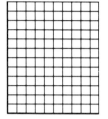

18. Graph the equation $y = -x^2 + 4$. Use the vertex and at least four other points. Use the diagram shown.

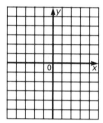

ANSWERS	
15. _____	(3)
16. _____	(3)
17. *See diagram.*	(5)
18. *See diagram.*	(5)
19. _____	(8)
20. _____	(8)
21. _____	(8)

CHALLENGE ANSWER

_____

Questions 19–21. Solve.

19. Hooke's Law states that the distance d that a spring is stretched by a hanging object varies directly as the weight W of the object. If a 6-kg weight stretches a particular spring 72 cm, how far will the spring stretch when $W = 4$ kg?

20. The current I in an electrical conductor varies inversely as the resistance R of the conductor. If the resistance is 250 ohms when the current is $\frac{1}{2}$ ampere, what is the current when the resistance is 400 ohms?

21. The centripetal force F on a body varies jointly as the mass m of the body and the square of its speed V. If $F = 1,350,000$ when $m = 60$ and $V = 300$, find m when $F = 1,920,000$ and $V = 400$.

CHALLENGE *(Optional)* The volume of a right circular cone varies jointly as its height and the square of its radius. Suppose that both the height of a cone and its radius are multiplied by n, and the volume of the cone becomes 216 times as great. What is the value of n?

Test 21—Test on Chapter 9 (Form B)

Questions 1–4. Find **(a)** the slope and **(b)** the y-intercept of the line determined by the given condition.

1. Its equation is $7x + y = 5$.

2. It contains the points $(6, 8)$ and $(3, 5)$.

3. Its equation is $4x - 7y = 0$.

4. It passes through the points $(4, -1)$ and $(-4, -1)$.

Questions 5–8. Write in standard form the equation of the line determined by the given condition.

5. It has zero slope and passes through the point $(0, 1)$.

6. It has no slope and passes through the origin.

7. It has slope $-\dfrac{2}{3}$ and y-intercept 1.

8. It contains the points $(1, 4)$ and $(5, 6)$.

Questions 9–10. (a) Change each equation to slope-intercept form. **(b)** Draw the graph using only the slope and y-intercept.

9. $3 = x - y$ 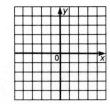 **10.** $3x + 2y = 4$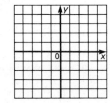

Questions 11–14. Determine whether or not each is a function.

11. $y = x^2 - 1$ **12.** $\{(1, 1), (2, 1), (3, 1)\}$

13. $y = 3x$ **14.** $\{(1, 1), (1, 2), (1, 3)\}$

ANSWERS

1. a. _____ (2)
 b. _____ (2)
2. a. _____ (2)
 b. _____ (2)
3. a. _____ (2)
 b. _____ (2)
4. a. _____ (2)
 b. _____ (2)
5. _____ (4)
6. _____ (4)
7. _____ (4)
8. _____ (4)
9. a. _____ (4)
 b. *See diagram.* (4)
10. a. _____ (4)
 b. *See diagram.* (4)
11. _____ (3)
12. _____ (3)
13. _____ (3)
14. _____ (3)

(continued)

ALGEBRA, Structure and Method, Book 1

Test 21—Test on Chapter 9 *(continued)*

Questions 15–17. $\{(1, 3), (2, 7), (3, 5), (4, 12), (5, 5), (6, 8)\}$ describes a function.

15. State the domain.

16. State the range.

17. Make a broken-line graph for the function. Use the diagram shown.

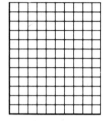

18. Graph the equation $y = x^2 - 4$. Use the vertex and at least four other points. Use the diagram shown.

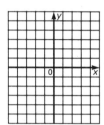

ANSWERS

15. _____ (3)

16. _____ (3)

17. *See diagram.* _____ (5)

18. *See diagram.* _____ (5)

19. _____ (8)

20. _____ (8)

21. _____ (8)

CHALLENGE ANSWER

_____

Questions 19–21. Solve.

19. Electric current I, measured in amperes, varies directly as the voltage V, measured in volts. When 110 volts are applied, the current is 22 amperes. What is the current when 135 volts are applied?

20. The intensity I of light from a light bulb varies inversely as the square of the distance d from the bulb. If $I = 90$ when the distance is 5 m, find I when the distance is 10 m.

21. The volume V of a pyramid varies jointly as its altitude h and the area of its base. A pyramid with a nine-inch square base and an altitude of 10 inches has a volume equal to 270 in^3. Find the volume of a pyramid with an altitude of 6 inches and a square base 4 inches on each side.

CHALLENGE *(Optional)* The volume of a circular cylinder varies jointly as its height and the square of its radius. Suppose that the radius of the cylinder is multiplied by n, the height is multiplied by $1.5n$, and the volume of the cylinder becomes 96 times as great. What is the value of n?

Test 22—Cumulative Test (Chapters 7–9)

Directions: Write answers in the spaces provided.

Questions 1–3. Simplify. Give answers in terms of positive exponents.

1. $\dfrac{21a^7b^{-3}}{33a^5b^{-5}}$

2. $(5x^{-1}y^2)^0$

3. $\dfrac{6g^2}{9g^3}$

Questions 4–5. Write each ratio in simplest form.

4. 0.4 m : 20 cm

5. The ratio of the area of an 8-inch by 12-inch rectangle to that of a 4-inch by 36-inch rectangle

Questions 6–7. Solve.

6. $\dfrac{n+3}{8} - \dfrac{n-2}{6} = 1$

7. $\dfrac{5}{x} = \dfrac{x-3}{2}$

8. What percent of 360 is 45?

9. 12 is 6% of what number?

10. Solve this system of equations by the graphic method:

$$x + y = 3$$
$$y = 1 + x$$

a. Graph the equations on the coordinate axes provided. Label each line with the corresponding equation.

b. Write the solution in the answer column.

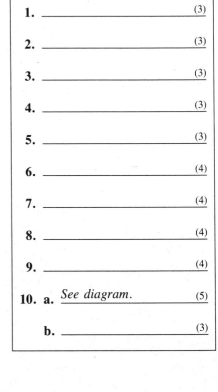

ANSWERS

1. _____ (3)

2. _____ (3)

3. _____ (3)

4. _____ (3)

5. _____ (3)

6. _____ (4)

7. _____ (4)

8. _____ (4)

9. _____ (4)

10. **a.** *See diagram.* (5)

   b. _____ (3)

(continued)

ALGEBRA, Structure and Method, Book 1

Test 22—Cumulative Test *(continued)*

11. The distance from the planet Pluto to the sun is 3,664,000,000 miles. Express this number of miles in scientific notation.

12. Solve this system of equations by whatever method you prefer.

$$2a + 5b = 18$$
$$3a + 4b = 27$$

13. Find the slope of the line passing through $(-1, 4)$ and $(3, 1)$.

14. Write an equation in standard form of the line whose slope is $\dfrac{1}{2}$ and whose y-intercept is -3.

15. (a) Change $x - y = 2$ to the slope-intercept form. (b) Then use the figure provided to draw the graph, using only the slope and y-intercept.

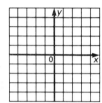

Questions 16–20. Solve.

16. Mr. Chan paid $6500 for a used car. In a year its value depreciated to $5200. By what percent had the car depreciated?

17. How much water must be evaporated from 100 gallons of a 4% brine solution to get a 5% brine solution?

18. One pump can fill a tank twice as fast as a second pump. If the pumps are used together, they will fill the tank in 16 minutes. How long would it take each pump working alone to fill the tank?

19. Flying against the wind, Mr. Guthrie's company plane flew 450 miles from one airport to another in $1\frac{1}{2}$ hours. The return trip, with no change in the wind's speed or direction, took $1\frac{1}{4}$ hours. What was the speed of the wind?

20. If Brian was twice as old as he is now, he would be 19 years older than Matthew is now. The sum of Brian's age at that time and Matthew's present age is 41. How old is each boy now?

ANSWERS

11. _____ (3)

12. _____ (6)

13. _____ (5)

14. _____ (5)

15. a. _____ (3)

 b. *See diagram.* (4)

16. _____ (7)

17. _____ (7)

18. _____ (7)

19. _____ (7)

20. _____

 _____ (7)

ALGEBRA, Structure and Method, Book 1
TESTS 49

NAME _____ DATE _____ SCORE _____

Test 23—Test on Chapter 10 (Form A)

Directions: Write answers in the spaces provided. For each matching or multiple-choice question, write the letter corresponding to the answer.

Questions 1–4. Translate each sentence into symbols.

1. 0 is greater than -3.

2. a is greater than or equal to 2.

3. -11 is less than -10.

4. x is not greater than 0.

Questions 5–8. Classify each statement as true or false.

5. $\left| -\dfrac{1}{2} \right| < \dfrac{1}{2}$

6. $|0| < |-10|$

7. $-3 < -2 < -1$

8. $-5 < 0 < -4$

Questions 9–12. Match each open sentence with the graph of its solution set. You will not use all the graphs.

9. $-x < 1$

A.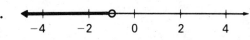

10. $x - 4 \geq -2$

B.

11. $\dfrac{y}{4} < \dfrac{1}{4}$

C.

12. $6k \neq 0$

D.

E.

Questions 13–18. Graph the solution set of each open sentence. Use the diagrams provided.

13. $|2y - 1| = 5$

14. $-4 \leq -1 + 3a < 11$

15. $|x - 3| < 1$

16. $-2 < -n < 2$

17. $|4x - 1| > -1$

18. $2m < 0$ or $3m > 6$

ANSWERS	
1. _____	(3)
2. _____	(3)
3. _____	(3)
4. _____	(3)
5. _____	(3)
6. _____	(3)
7. _____	(3)
8. _____	(3)
9. _____	(4)
10. _____	(4)
11. _____	(4)
12. _____	(4)
13. *See diagram.*	(6)
14. *See diagram.*	(6)
15. *See diagram.*	(6)
16. *See diagram.*	(6)
17. *See diagram.*	(6)
18. *See diagram.*	(6)

(continued)

Test 23—Test on Chapter 10   *(continued)*

19. Which inequality is graphed on the diagram shown?

A. $2x - y < 2$
B. $y - 2x < 2$
C. $2x - y \geq 2$
D. $2x - y > 2$
E. $y - 2x > 2$

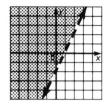

Questions 20–21. Refer to the following system of inequalities:

$$x - 3y < -2$$
$$x + y < 2$$

20. Graph the pair of inequalities and indicate their solution by crosshatching or shading. Use the diagram shown.

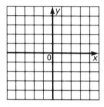

21. Which ordered pair does *not* belong to the solution set of the system?

A. $(-1, 1)$ **B.** $(-1, 2)$ **C.** $(1, 1)$

D. $(0, 1)$ **E.** $(-2, 2)$

CHALLENGE *(Optional)* Find all sets of four consecutive odd integers whose sum is between -10 and 20.

ANSWERS

19. _____ (8)

20. *See diagram.* (12)

21. _____ (4)

CHALLENGE ANSWERS

_____

_____

_____

Test 24—Test on Chapter 10 (Form B)

Directions: Write answers in the spaces provided. For each matching or multiple-choice question, write the letter corresponding to the answer.

Questions 1–4. Translate each sentence into symbols.

1. -1 is greater than -2.

2. b is less than or equal to 2.

3. a is not less than b.

4. -5 is less than 0.

Questions 5–8. Classify each statement as true or false.

5. $|-7| < |7|$

6. $|3| > |-1|$

7. $-5 > 0 > 5$

8. $|0| < |-1|$

Questions 9–12. Match each open sentence with the graph of its solution set. You will not use all the graphs.

9. $-3x < 3$

10. $2m - 3 > -7$

11. $-\dfrac{y}{2} > -\dfrac{1}{2}$

12. $3t \neq 6$

A.

B.

C.

D.

E.

Questions 13–18. Graph the solution set of each open sentence. Use the diagrams provided.

13. $|2x + 1| = 3$

14. $-2 < 1 - 3a \leq 1$

15. $|3x| < 9$

16. $-3 < -b < 3$

17. $|x - 5| > -5$

18. $3m < -3$ or $5m > 5$

ANSWERS	
1. _____	(3)
2. _____	(3)
3. _____	(3)
4. _____	(3)
5. _____	(3)
6. _____	(3)
7. _____	(3)
8. _____	(3)
9. _____	(4)
10. _____	(4)
11. _____	(4)
12. _____	(4)
13. *See diagram.*	(6)
14. *See diagram.*	(6)
15. *See diagram.*	(6)
16. *See diagram.*	(6)
17. *See diagram.*	(6)
18. *See diagram.*	(6)

(continued)

ALGEBRA, Structure and Method, Book 1

Test 24—Test on Chapter 10 (continued)

19. Which inequality is graphed on the diagram shown?

   A. $2x - 3y \geq -6$
   B. $3x - 2y < -6$
   C. $3x - 2y \geq -6$
   D. $2y - 3x \geq -6$
   E. $2y - 3x \leq -6$

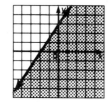

Questions 20–21. Refer to the following system of inequalities:

$$x + 2 \geq y$$
$$3x + y \leq 6$$

20. Graph the pair of inequalities and indicate their solution by cross-hatching or shading. Use the diagram shown.

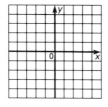

21. Which ordered pair does *not* belong to the solution set of the system?

   A. $(0, 0)$ **B.** $(2, 0)$ **C.** $(-2, 0)$

   D. $(0, 3)$ **E.** $(1, 3)$

CHALLENGE *(Optional)* Find all sets of four consecutive even integers whose sum is between -40 and 0.

ANSWERS

19. _____ (8)

20. *See diagram.* _____ (12)

21. _____ (4)

CHALLENGE ANSWERS

_____

_____

_____

_____

_____

Test 25—Test on Chapter 11 (Form A)

Directions: Write answers in the spaces provided.

Questions 1–2. Replace the ___?___ with $<$, $=$, or $>$ to make a true statement.

1. $\dfrac{8}{15}$ ___?___ $\dfrac{7}{16}$

2. $17\frac{1}{3}$ ___?___ $\dfrac{400}{12}$

3. Find a rational number halfway between $\dfrac{1}{3}$ and $\dfrac{5}{8}$.

Questions 4–5. Express each fraction as a terminating or repeating decimal.

4. $\dfrac{5}{6}$

5. $\dfrac{5}{16}$

Questions 6–7. Express each rational number as a fraction in simplest form.

6. $0.\overline{27}$

7. 0.444

Questions 8–9. Find the indicated square roots.

8. $\sqrt{484}$

9. $\sqrt{\dfrac{169}{441}}$

Questions 10–11. Use this table of square roots as necessary.

10. Approximate $\sqrt{504}$ to the nearest hundredth.

11. Approximate $\sqrt{27{,}000}$ to the nearest unit.

$\sqrt{1} = 1$	$\sqrt{6} \approx 2.449$
$\sqrt{2} \approx 1.414$	$\sqrt{7} \approx 2.646$
$\sqrt{3} \approx 1.732$	$\sqrt{8} \approx 2.828$
$\sqrt{4} = 2$	$\sqrt{9} = 3$
$\sqrt{5} \approx 2.236$	$\sqrt{10} \approx 3.162$

Questions 12–13. Simplify.

12. $\sqrt{468}$

13. $\sqrt{425m^6 n^{10}}$

14. Solve: $12x^2 - 27 = 0$

ANSWERS

1. _____ (2)
2. _____ (2)
3. _____ (2)
4. _____ (2)
5. _____ (2)
6. _____ (2)
7. _____ (2)
8. _____ (2)
9. _____ (3)
10. _____ (3)
11. _____ (3)
12. _____ (3)
13. _____ (3)
14. _____ (3)

(continued)

ALGEBRA, Structure and Method, Book 1
Copyright © 1986 by Houghton Mifflin Company. All rights reserved. Printed in U.S.A.

Test 25—Test on Chapter 11 *(continued)*

Questions 15–16. State whether or not the three numbers given could represent the lengths of the sides of a right triangle.

15. 4, 7, 8   **16.** 15, 36, 39

Questions 17–20. Refer to the right triangle shown. Find the missing length correct to the nearest hundredth.

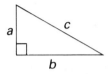

17. $a = 3$, $b = 7$, $c = \underline{\ ?\ }$ **18.** $a = 2$, $b = \underline{\ ?\ }$, $c = 12$

19. $a = \underline{\ ?\ }$, $b = 9$, $c = 15$ **20.** $a = 7$, $b = 15$, $c = \underline{\ ?\ }$

21. The diagonal of a square measures $7\sqrt{2}$ cm. Find the length of a side of the square.

Questions 22–25. Simplify.

22. $\sqrt{\dfrac{5}{8}} \cdot \sqrt{\dfrac{3}{2}}$ **23.** $\dfrac{6\sqrt{3}}{\sqrt{12}}$

24. $\sqrt{6} - \sqrt{\dfrac{3}{2}}$ **25.** $\sqrt{5} + \sqrt{20} + \sqrt{45}$

Questions 26–29. Simplify. Assume that all variables represent positive real numbers.

26. $(-5\sqrt{ab^2})(-3\sqrt{a})$ **27.** $(2\sqrt{3} - 5)(2\sqrt{3} + 3)$

28. $(3 - \sqrt{2})^2$ **29.** $\sqrt{3}(\sqrt{12} + 3)$

30. Rationalize the denominator of $\dfrac{5}{2\sqrt{3} + 1}$.

31. Solve $\sqrt{2x - 3} = 7$.

CHALLENGE *(Optional)* Solve $\sqrt{20 - x} + 8 = \sqrt{9 - x} + 11$.

ANSWERS

15. _____ (3)

16. _____ (3)

17. _____ (4)

18. _____ (4)

19. _____ (4)

20. _____ (4)

21. _____ (4)

22. _____ (4)

23. _____ (4)

24. _____ (4)

25. _____ (4)

26. _____ (4)

27. _____ (4)

28. _____ (4)

29. _____ (4)

30. _____ (4)

31. _____ (4)

CHALLENGE ANSWER

_____

Test 26—Test on Chapter 11 (Form B)

Directions: Write the answers in the spaces provided.

Questions 1–2. Replace the ___?___ with $<$, $=$, or $>$ to make a true statement.

1. $\dfrac{5}{13}$ ___?___ $\dfrac{6}{14}$

2. $5\frac{5}{6}$ ___?___ $\dfrac{140}{24}$

3. Find a rational number halfway between $\dfrac{1}{7}$ and $\dfrac{2}{5}$.

Questions 4–5. Express each fraction as a terminating or repeating decimal.

4. $\dfrac{3}{8}$

5. $\dfrac{5}{12}$

Questions 6–7. Express each rational number as a fraction in simplest form.

6. $0.\overline{65}$

7. 0.555

Questions 8–9. Find the indicated square roots.

8. $\sqrt{324}$

9. $\sqrt{\dfrac{81}{324}}$

Questions 10–11. Use this table of square roots as necessary.

10. Approximate $\sqrt{540}$ to the nearest hundredth.

11. Approximate $\sqrt{36,000}$ to the nearest unit.

$\sqrt{1} = 1$	$\sqrt{6} \approx 2.449$
$\sqrt{2} \approx 1.414$	$\sqrt{7} \approx 2.646$
$\sqrt{3} \approx 1.732$	$\sqrt{8} \approx 2.828$
$\sqrt{4} = 2$	$\sqrt{9} = 3$
$\sqrt{5} \approx 2.236$	$\sqrt{10} \approx 3.162$

Questions 12–13. Simplify.

12. $\sqrt{700}$

13. $\sqrt{512m^2n^8}$

14. *Solve*: $12x^2 - 75 = 0$

ANSWERS

1. _____ (2)
2. _____ (2)
3. _____ (2)
4. _____ (2)
5. _____ (2)
6. _____ (2)
7. _____ (2)
8. _____ (2)
9. _____ (3)
10. _____ (3)
11. _____ (3)
12. _____ (3)
13. _____ (3)
14. _____ (3)

(continued)

ALGEBRA, Structure and Method, Book 1

Test 26—Test on Chapter 11 *(continued)*

Questions 15–16. State whether or not the three numbers given could represent the lengths of the sides of a right triangle.

15. 1.5, 2, 2.5

16. 5, 9, 10

Questions 17–20. Refer to the right triangle shown. Find the missing length correct to the nearest hundredth.

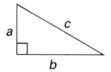

17. $a = 2$, $b = 4$, $c = \underline{\ ?\ }$

18. $a = 3$, $b = \underline{\ ?\ }$, $c = 12$

19. $a = 5$, $b = 9$, $c = \underline{\ ?\ }$

20. $a = \underline{\ ?\ }$, $b = 8$, $c = 15$

21. A side of a square measures $2\sqrt{2}$ cm. Find the length of the diagonal of the square.

Questions 22–25. Simplify.

22. $\sqrt{\dfrac{3}{8}} \cdot \sqrt{\dfrac{1}{2}}$

23. $\dfrac{7\sqrt{2}}{\sqrt{8}}$

24. $\sqrt{8} - \sqrt{\dfrac{1}{2}}$

25. $\sqrt{7} + \sqrt{28} + \sqrt{63}$

Questions 26–29. Simplify. Assume that all variables represent positive real numbers.

26. $(-3\sqrt{a^2b^2})(-5\sqrt{a})$

27. $(5\sqrt{2} - 4)(5\sqrt{2} + 1)$

28. $(5 - \sqrt{7})^2$

29. $\sqrt{3}(\sqrt{27} + 5)$

30. Rationalize the denominator of $\dfrac{1}{3\sqrt{5} - 1}$.

31. Solve $4\sqrt{5t + 5} = 20$.

CHALLENGE *(Optional)* Solve $4 + \sqrt{10 - x} = 6 + \sqrt{4 - x}$

ANSWERS

15. _____ (3)

16. _____ (3)

17. _____ (4)

18. _____ (4)

19. _____ (4)

20. _____ (4)

21. _____ (4)

22. _____ (4)

23. _____ (4)

24. _____ (4)

25. _____ (4)

26. _____ (4)

27. _____ (4)

28. _____ (4)

29. _____ (4)

30. _____ (4)

31. _____ (4)

CHALLENGE ANSWER

_____

Test 27—Test on Chapter 12 (Form A)

Directions: Write answers in the spaces provided. Write all irrational expressions in simplest radical form.

Questions 1–2. Write each trinomial as the square of a binomial.

1. $x^2 - 12x + 36$

2. $x^2 + 18x + 81$

Questions 3–4. Complete the square.

3. $x^2 + 14x + \underline{}$

4. $x^2 - x + \underline{}$

Questions 5–6. Solve each equation by completing the square.

5. $x^2 + 6x = 4$

6. $x^2 + 8x + 5 = 0$

7. Write the values of a, b, and c (as used in the quadratic formula) for the equation $5x^2 - x = -3$.

Questions 8–9. Solve by the quadratic formula. If an equation has no solution, write "no solution."

8. $2x^2 + 5x + 1 = 0$

9. $5x^2 - 4x + 1 = 0$

Questions 10–13. (a) Write the value of the discriminant of each equation. (b) Then use it to decide how many different real number roots the equation has. (Do not solve.)

10. $3x^2 - x - 1 = 0$

11. $x^2 = 2x - 1$

12. $7x^2 + 1 = -5x$

13. $x = 1 - x^2$

Questions 14–19. Solve by any method you prefer.

14. $u^2 - 15u = -1$

15. $3w^2 - 16 = 0$

16. $x^2 + 8x + 5 = 0$

17. $m^2 = 4m$

18. $2x^2 + 12x = -18$

19. $y^2 - 4y + 3 = 0$

ANSWERS

1. _____ (2)

2. _____ (2)

3. _____ (2)

4. _____ (2)

5. _____ (5)

6. _____ (5)

7. _____ (3)

8. _____ (5)

9. _____ (5)

10. a. _____ (1)

 b. _____ (2)

11. a. _____ (1)

 b. _____ (2)

12. a. _____ (1)

 b. _____ (2)

13. a. _____ (1)

 b. _____ (2)

14. _____ (5)

15. _____ (5)

16. _____ (5)

17. _____ (5)

18. _____ (5)

19. _____ (5)

(continued)

ALGEBRA, Structure and Method, Book 1

Test 27—Test on Chapter 12 (continued)

Questions 20–24. Solve. Give irrational roots to the nearest tenth. Use a table of square roots or a calculator as necessary.

20. The difference of a number and its square is 12. Find the number.

21. The length of a rectangle is 3 cm greater than its width. The area of the rectangle is 180 cm². Find the length and the width.

22. If the sides of a square plot of ground are increased by 1 m, its area becomes 225 m². Find the length of the sides of the original plot.

23. Together Anna and Carla can spray-paint a van in 8 hours. Alone it takes Anna 2 hours less than Carla. Find the time it takes each of them to paint the van alone. Give your answers to the nearest tenth of an hour.

24. The Hillside School Drama Club planned a field trip to see a play. The bus they hired to transport them cost $150. If there had been 10 more students in the club, each would have had to pay $1.25 less as his or her share of the cost. How many students were in the club?

CHALLENGE *(Optional)* Find the solution set of the inequality $5m^2 > 12 - 4m$.

ANSWERS	
20. _____	(5)
21. _____	
_____	(5)
22. _____	(5)
23. _____	
_____	(6)
24. _____	(6)
CHALLENGE ANSWER	
_____	

Test 28—Test on Chapter 12 (Form B)

Directions: Write answers in the spaces provided. Write all irrational expressions in simplest radical form.

ANSWERS

Questions 1–2. Write each trinomial as the square of a binomial.

1. $x^2 - 20x + 100$ **2.** $x^2 + 16x + 64$

Questions 3–4. Complete the square.

3. $x^2 + 30x + \underline{\ ?\ }$ **4.** $x^2 - 2x + \underline{\ ?\ }$

Questions 5–6. Solve each equation by completing the square.

5. $x^2 + 4x + 2 = 0$ **6.** $x^2 = 2x + 1$

7. Write the values of a, b, and c (as used in the quadratic formula) for the equation $3x^2 - 1 = 2x$.

Questions 8–9. Solve by the quadratic formula. If an equation has no solution, write "no solution."

8. $3x^2 - x - 1 = 0$ **9.** $4x^2 + 2x + 3 = 0$

Questions 10–13. (a) Write the value of the discriminant of each equation. **(b)** Then use it to decide how many different real number roots the equation has. (Do not solve.)

10. $3x^2 - 4 = x$ **11.** $x^2 + 5 = -3x$

12. $4x^2 - 12x + 9 = 0$ **13.** $3x^2 + x = 1$

Questions 14–19. Solve by any method you prefer.

14. $x^2 - 3x - 40 = 0$ **15.** $5x^2 - 125 = 0$

16. $x^2 - x = 1$ **17.** $x^2 + 6x + 8 = 0$

18. $x^2 - 5x + 6 = 0$ **19.** $6x^2 - 5x = 1$

1. _____ (2)
2. _____ (2)
3. _____ (2)
4. _____ (2)
5. _____ (5)
6. _____ (5)
7. _____ (3)
8. _____ (5)
9. _____ (5)
10. a. _____ (1)
    b. _____ (2)
11. a. _____ (1)
    b. _____ (2)
12. a. _____ (1)
    b. _____ (2)
13. a. _____ (1)
    b. _____ (2)
14. _____ (5)
15. _____ (5)
16. _____ (5)
17. _____ (5)
18. _____ (5)
19. _____ (5)

(continued)

ALGEBRA, Structure and Method, Book 1
Copyright © 1986 by Houghton Mifflin Company. All rights reserved. Printed in U.S.A.

Test 28—Test on Chapter 12 *(continued)*

Questions 20–24. Solve. Give irrational roots to the nearest tenth. Use a table of square roots or a calculator as necessary.

20. The difference of a number and its square is 210. Find the number.

21. The width of a rectangle is 5 cm less than its length. The area of the rectangle is 300 cm². Find the length and the width.

22. If the sides of a square piece of tile are decreased by 3 cm, its area becomes 289 cm². Find the length of the sides of the original piece of tile.

23. Together Janice and Roger can wash and wax Janice's car in 50 minutes. Alone it takes Janice 10 minutes less than Roger. Find the number of minutes, to the nearest minute, it takes each of them to wash and wax the car alone.

24. A group of students hired a bus to take them to an "away" football game. The cost of renting the bus was $140. If 15 more students had joined them, each would have had to pay $1.20 less as his or her share of the cost. How many students went in the bus to see the game?

ANSWERS

20. _____ (5)

21. _____

_____ (5)

22. _____ (5)

23. _____

_____ (6)

24. _____ (6)

CHALLENGE ANSWER

_____

CHALLENGE *(Optional)* Find the solution set of the inequality $2n^2 < n + 15$.

Test 29—Cumulative Test (Chapters 10–12)

Directions: Write answers in the spaces provided.

Questions 1–12. Express in simplest form.

1. $\sqrt{3}(2\sqrt{2} - 3\sqrt{3})$

2. $\sqrt{32}$

3. $\dfrac{2}{3}\sqrt{162}$

4. $\dfrac{2\sqrt{49}}{3\sqrt{40}}$

5. $6\sqrt{18} - 2\sqrt{98} + 2\sqrt{9}$

6. $(2\sqrt{5} + 5)^2$

7. $\sqrt{500}$

8. $\dfrac{2\sqrt{a^3 b^7}}{\sqrt{8a^5 b^5}}$

9. $\dfrac{2}{\sqrt{6} + 2}$

10. $(4 - \sqrt{5})(4 + \sqrt{5})$

11. $\dfrac{6}{5\sqrt{12}}$

12. $3\sqrt{6} + 6\sqrt{\dfrac{1}{6}} - 8\sqrt{1.5}$

13. Express $\dfrac{37}{16}$ as a decimal.

14. Express 0.297 as a fraction in simplest terms.

Questions 15–18. **(a)** Solve. **(b)** Graph the solution set. Use the diagrams provided.

15. $5x + 3 > 4x - 2$

16. $2 < x + 3 \le 6$

17. $|2x + 3| \le 3$

18. $x + 1 \le -2$ or $x + 1 > 2$

ANSWERS

1. _____ (3)

2. _____ (3)

3. _____ (3)

4. _____ (3)

5. _____ (3)

6. _____ (3)

7. _____ (3)

8. _____ (3)

9. _____ (3)

10. _____ (3)

11. _____ (3)

12. _____ (3)

13. _____ (3)

14. _____ (2)

15. a. _____ (2)

   b. _See diagram._ (1)

16. a. _____ (2)

   b. _See diagram._ (1)

17. a. _____ (2)

   b. _See diagram._ (1)

18. a. _____ (2)

   b. _See diagram._ (1)

(continued)

ALGEBRA, Structure and Method, Book 1

Test 29—Cumulative Test *(continued)*

Questions 19–26. Solve by whatever method you prefer.

19. $x^2 = 11 - x$

20. $27 - y^2 = 0$

21. $\sqrt{\dfrac{9x}{2}} - 2 = 7$

22. $3x^2 + 5x + 1 = 0$

23. $\sqrt{a^2 + 9} = a + 3$

24. $y^2 + 10y + 25 = 9$

25. $y^2 - 4y + 3 = 0$

26. $9s = s^3$

Questions 27–29. Solve. Approximate irrational roots to the nearest tenth. Use the table provided.

27. The total area of the six faces of a cube is 240 cm². How long, to the nearest tenth, is one edge?

n	$\sqrt{n}$	n	$\sqrt{n}$
1	1.000	6	2.449
2	1.414	7	2.646
3	1.732	8	2.828
4	2.000	9	3.000
5	2.236	10	3.162

28. A rectangle has a perimeter of 28 feet, and the length of a diagonal is 10 feet. What are its dimensions?

29. A faucet can fill a tub in 20 minutes, and a drain can empty the tub in 40 minutes. If both the faucet and the drain are opened, how long will it take to fill the tub?

ANSWERS

19. _____ (4)

20. _____ (4)

21. _____ (4)

22. _____ (4)

23. _____ (4)

24. _____ (4)

25. _____ (4)

26. _____ (4)

27. _____ (5)

28. _____ (5)

29. _____ (5)

Test 30—Cumulative Test (Chapters 7–12)

Directions: Write answers in the spaces provided.

Questions 1–10. Simplify. If an answer involves exponents, write the answer in terms of positive exponents.

1. $(6\sqrt{15} + \sqrt{5})(2\sqrt{15} - 3\sqrt{5})$

2. two yards : 15 inches

3. $\sqrt{300}$

4. $\dfrac{\sqrt{6} - 1}{3 + \sqrt{6}}$

5. $\dfrac{-13g^2h^{-3}}{-39g^{-5}h}$

6. $2\sqrt{50} - 3\sqrt{18}$

7. $(y^2 - 4) : (y + 2)^2$

8. $\sqrt{\dfrac{3}{40}}$

9. $(-5\sqrt{14})(-\sqrt{7})(\sqrt{8})$

10. $[-(c^\circ)]^5$

11. Express 1,300,000,000 m (the diameter of the sun) in scientific notation.

12. Express $\dfrac{4}{11}$ as a decimal.

13. Express $0.5\overline{7}$ as a fraction in simplest form.

Questions 14–15. Graph the solution set.

14. $y - 2 = x$

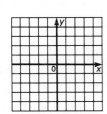

15. $y = \dfrac{1}{3}x$

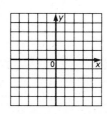

ANSWERS	
1. _____	(2)
2. _____	(2)
3. _____	(2)
4. _____	(2)
5. _____	(2)
6. _____	(2)
7. _____	(2)
8. _____	(2)
9. _____	(2)
10. _____	(2)
11. _____	(1)
12. _____	(1)
13. _____	(1)
14. *See diagram.*	(2)
15. *See diagram.*	(2)

(continued)

ALGEBRA, Structure and Method, Book 1

Test 30—Cumulative Test *(continued)*

Questions 16–20. Graph the solution set.

16. $-3 \leq x + 1 < 5$

17. $7x - 1 < 6x + 1$

18. $|2x + 1| \leq 5$

19. $5 - 2v > 7$ or $4v < v + 9$

20. $x + 2y \geq -4$

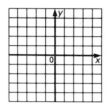

Questions 21–30. Solve each equation or system.

21. $\dfrac{4}{3t - 2} + \dfrac{7}{3t} - \dfrac{1}{t} = 0$

22. $3x^2 - 2x - 9 = 0$

23. $\sqrt{\dfrac{3x - 5}{4}} - 2 = 0$

24. $3x^2 + 5x = 0$

25. $\sqrt{b^2 - 16} = b - 4$

26. $3x(x + 1) - 7x(x + 2) = 6$

27. $3x^2 + x - 2 = 0$

28. $\dfrac{3}{s + 1} + \dfrac{1}{s - 1} = 2$

29. $9q - 8r = 1$
$6q + 12r = 5$

30. $y = 2x - 8$
$x = 3y - 6$

ANSWERS	
16. _See diagram._	(2)
17. _See diagram._	(2)
18. _See diagram._	(2)
19. _See diagram._	(2)
20. _See diagram._	(2)
21. _____	(3)
22. _____	(3)
23. _____	(3)
24. _____	(3)
25. _____	(3)
26. _____	(3)
27. _____	(3)
28. _____	(3)
29. _____	(3)
30. _____	(3)

(continued)

Test 30—Cumulative Test *(continued)*

Questions 31–33. Write in standard form the equation for the line described.

31. It has a slope of $\dfrac{3}{2}$ and passes through the point $(-1, -6)$.

32. It is parallel to the line $3x - y = 2$ and passes through the point $(2, 4)$.

33. It contains the points $(1, 6)$ and $(-1, -9)$.

Questions 34–39. Solve.

34. Rod A is divided by marks into 100 equal parts. It has the same length as rod B, which is marked into 80 equal parts. How many parts on rod B have the same length as 60 parts on rod A?

35. How many liters of pure disinfectant must be added to 85 liters of a 5% disinfectant solution to produce a 15% solution?

36. The tens digit of a two-digit number is 2 less than the units digit. Three times the square of the tens digit increased by the sum of both digits equals the number itself. Find the number.

37. If 7 is added to both the numerator and denominator of a fraction, the result equals $\dfrac{4}{5}$. If 7 is subtracted from both numerator and denominator, the result equals $\dfrac{2}{3}$. Find the original fraction.

38. A three-quarter-inch wire has 12 ohms resistance. How much resistance has the same length of half-inch wire, if resistance varies inversely as the square of the diameter?

39. Each of two incinerators can process a day's refuse in 20 hours. Together with a third incinerator, they process the refuse in 6 hours. In what amount of time can the third incinerator do the job alone?

ANSWERS	
31. _____	(3)
32. _____	(3)
33. _____	(3)
34. _____	(4)
35. _____	(4)
36. _____	(4)
37. _____	(4)
38. _____	(4)
39. _____	(4)

ALGEBRA, Structure and Method, Book 1

Variables; Grouping Symbols (For use after Section 1–2)

Select each answer from the choices in parentheses. Write the answer in the blank.

1. *ab* means *a* _____ *b*.   (*plus, divided by, times*)

2. $\dfrac{a}{b}$ means *a* _____ *b*.   (*plus, divided by, times*)

3. *a* _____ *b* means *a* is not equal to *b*.   ($=$, $\neq$, $\cdot$)

4. Parentheses are an example of a _____.   (*grouping symbol, value, variable*)

Simplify each expression.

5. $7 + (12 - 3)$ _____

6. $(18 - 3) \div (3 + 2)$ _____

7. $(7 \times 3) - (5 \cdot 4)$ _____

8. $10 - (3 + 4)$ _____

Evaluate each expression if $x = 3$, $y = 5$, $z = 4$, and $a = 2$.

9. $ax + ay$ _____

10. $3a(x + y)$ _____

11. $(z - x) - (x - a)$ _____

12. $\dfrac{x + 3z}{ay}$ _____

Simplify each expression.

13. $5 \times 3 \times 3 \times 6 \times 6$ _____

14. $24 - [63 \div (6 + 3)]$ _____

15. $15 - (5 \times 3)$ _____

16. $20(12 - 8) - 30 \div (10 + 5)$ _____

17. $\dfrac{36 \div 12 + 6}{8 - 5}$ _____

18. $15 - 5 \times 2 + 8 \div 4$ _____

Simplify the expression on each side of the _?_. Then make a true statement by replacing the _?_ with the symbol $=$ or $\neq$.

19. $\dfrac{16 \times 3}{8 + 4}$ _?_ $\dfrac{9 + 3}{4 - 1}$ _____

20. $(8 - 3 \times 2)$ _?_ $(8 - 3) \times 2$ _____

21. $3(5 + 2)$ _?_ $3 \times 5 + 2$ _____

22. $1 + \dfrac{16 + 4}{3 + 2}$ _?_ $\dfrac{8 + 4 \times 3}{8 - 2 - 2}$ _____

Equations; Words into Symbols; Solving Problems

(For use after Section 1–6)

Select each answer from the choices in parentheses. Write the answer in the blank.

1. The solution of an equation is also called the _____. *(root, domain, side)*

2. The set of all solutions of an open sentence is called the _____. *(domain, solution set, expression)*

3. The given set of numbers that a variable may represent is called the _____ of the variable. *(root, solution set, domain)*

Solve each equation if $x \in \{0, 1, 2, 3, 4, 5, 6, 7\}$. If no value in the domain satisfies the equation, write "no solution."

4. $2x = 6$ _____

5. $x + 5 = 11$ _____

6. $3x = 5$ _____

7. $\frac{2}{3}x = 4$ _____

Represent the required numbers in terms of the given variables.

8. What number is seven less than twice the number n? _____

9. The difference between two numbers is eight. The smaller is x. What is the larger number? _____

Write an equation for each sentence.

10. The sum of the number x and three is five. _____

11. Five less than the number y is two. _____

12. The sum of 16 and three times the number r is 64. _____

13. An old house was sold for $96,000, which was four times its original selling price, p. _____

Use the five-step plan to solve this problem.

14. In a choral group of 28 students, there are 8 more girls than boys. How many boys are in the group? _____

ALGEBRA, Structure and Method, Book 1

Number Lines; Opposites; Absolute Values; Comparing Numbers (For use after Section 1–9)

Select each answer from the choices in parentheses. Write the answer in the blank.

1. If A and B are two points on a number line and $A > B$, then A is located to the _____ of B. *(left, right)*

2. 0 is the smallest _____ number. *(positive, whole, real)*

3. The absolute value of a number is never _____. *(positive, negative, zero)*

Exercises 4–11 refer to the number line below.

Name the coordinates of the given points.

4. B _____ **5.** E _____ **6.** H _____ **7.** K _____

List the letters for the points whose coordinates are given.

8. -3 _____ **9.** 0 _____ **10.** 5 _____ **11.** -6 _____

Simplify.

12. $-(-13)$ _____ **13.** $-|-11|$ _____ **14.** $|-(-1)| - |-1|$ _____

Give the solution set of each equation over the set of real numbers. If there is no solution, write "no solution."

15. $|x| = 11$ _____ **16.** $|3a| = -12$ _____

17. $|-x| = 5$ _____ **18.** $3 - |t| = 2$ _____

Translate each statement into symbols.

19. Zero is greater than negative fifteen. _____

20. The opposite of two is greater than the opposite of three. _____

Replace each __?__ with one of the symbols $<$ or $>$ to make a true statement.

21. $|-3|$ __?__ $|-5|$ _____ **22.** $-(-7)$ __?__ $-|7|$ _____

23. -5.9 __?__ -5.8 _____ **24.** $-|15|$ __?__ $|-15|$ _____

Basic Assumptions; Addition (For use after Section 2–3)

Match each statement with the axiom or property it illustrates. (You will not use all the axioms or properties.)

1. _____ $5 \cdot y = y \cdot 5$ **A.** Commutative axiom

2. _____ $a + -a = 0$ **B.** Associative axiom

3. _____ $(a + b) + c = a + (b + c)$ **C.** Closure axiom

4. _____ $a = a$ **D.** Identity axiom for addition

5. _____ If $x = 5$, then $5 = x$.   **E.** Axiom of opposites

6. _____ If $x = 5$ and $y = 5$, then $x = y$. **F.** Reflexive property of equality

7. _____ $a + b$ is a real number.   **G.** Symmetric property of equality

                                                H. Transitive property of equality

Simplify each expression.

8. $397 + 29 + 3 + 1$ _____   9. $5 \times 37 \times 2 \times 10$ _____

10. $0.7 + 6.9 + 1.3$ _____   11. $12 \times 14 \times 4 \times 25$ _____

12. $7 \times a \times 6$ _____   13. $35\frac{3}{4} + \frac{7}{8} + 4\frac{1}{4} + \frac{1}{8}$ _____

Simplify each expression. If necessary, use a number line such as the one below to help you.

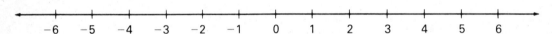

14. $(-5 + 4) + 1$ _____   15. $(-3 + 7) + 2$ _____

16. $[8 + (-2)] + 6$ _____   17. $(-5 + 8) + (-1)$ _____

Add.

18. $-8 + 45 + (-7) + (-6)$ _____   19. $-85 + 12 + 53 + (-5)$ _____

Evaluate each expression if $x = -5$, $y = |-2|$, and $z = -2$.

20. $x + y + (-3)$ _____   21. $x + (y + z)$ _____

22. $-x + (-y) + (-z)$ _____   23. $-12 + (-x) + z$ _____

Replace each __?__ with a number to make a true statement.

24. $\underline{\ ?\ } + -7 = -2$ _____   25. $-0.6 + \underline{\ ?\ } = 1$ _____

26. $7 + \underline{\ ?\ } = -11$ _____   27. $0.75 + \underline{\ ?\ } = -3.25$ _____

ALGEBRA, Structure and Method, Book 1

Subtraction; The Distributive Axiom (For use after Section 2–5)

Select each answer from the choices in parentheses. Write the answer in the blank.

1. Subtracting a real number m is the same as _____ the opposite of m. *(adding, subtracting)*

2. The opposite of $x + 7$ is _____. $(-x + 7, -x - 7, x - 7)$

3. The distributive axiom states that $a(b + c) =$ _____. $(ab + c, a + bc, ab + ac)$

Simplify.

4. $8 - 15$ _____

5. $16 - (-8)$ _____

6. $-4.3 - 2.1$ _____

7. $(15 - 27) - (1 - 4)$ _____

8. $2 + (-3) - (-1)$ _____

9. $-13 - 4 - [-5 - (-7)]$ _____

10. The difference of -17 and -3 decreased by -5. _____

Evaluate each expression if $a = -5$, $b = 3$, and $c = -2$.

11. $a - b - c$ _____

12. $c - |a - b|$ _____

13. $b - |a| - |c|$ _____

14. $|c - b| - a$ _____

Simplify.

15. $37n + 15n$ _____

16. $27c - 31c$ _____

17. $7(x + 5) + 1$ _____

18. $(-5)y + 14 + 8y - 7$ _____

19. $3t - 6 - 5t + 11$ _____

20. $3(a + 2b) + 4(3a - 5b)$ _____

Represent each word phrase by a variable expression. Then simplify it.

21. Five times the sum of a and b, decreased by three times b. _____

22. Twelve more than four times the sum of x and two. _____

23. Six more than the sum of negative eleven and $5y$, increased by one half the difference of $4y$ and two. _____

Multiplication; Consecutive Integers (For use after Section 2–7)

Select each answer from the choices in parentheses. Write the answer in the blank.

1. The multiplicative property of zero states that any number times zero

   equals _____. *(the number, zero)*

2. The multiplicative property of negative one states that any number times negative one equals

   _____. *(zero, the opposite of the number, one)*

3. The product of a positive number and a negative number is _____. *(positive, negative, zero)*

4. The product of two negative numbers is _____. *(positive, negative, zero)*

Simplify.

5. $(-3a)(4b)$ _____

6. $(-9)(-10)(-11)$ _____

7. $(18)(0)(-7)$ _____

8. $3(-2c + 8)$ _____

9. $(-5)(2x - 3)$ _____

10. $(-12) \times (-1) \times [(-15) \times (-3)]$ _____

11. $3t + 5 - 2t - 7$ _____

12. $-3(2x - 1) + 5(3 - 4x)$ _____

13. $4(x - 5) - 5(x + 3)$ _____

14. $(-a)(-b)(-c)(-d)(e)$ _____

15. $(-5)(-x + 3) + 10$ _____

16. $-3(-5 - y) + 2(-y + 3)$ _____

17. $n + (n + 1) + 3n$ _____

18. $3x + 5 - 2(x - 3)$ _____

Write an equation to represent the stated relationship among integers.

19. The sum of three consecutive integers is 60. _____

20. The sum of two consecutive even integers is 46. _____

21. The sum of two consecutive odd integers is 40. _____

22. The sum of four consecutive odd integers is 32. _____

23. There are three consecutive integers. The sum of the first and the third is equal to twice the second. _____

24. The sum of five consecutive integers is zero. _____

ALGEBRA, Structure and Method, Book 1

Reciprocals; Division (For use after Section 2–9)

Select each answer from the choices in parentheses. Write the answer in the blank.

1. The product of a real number and its reciprocal is _____. $(-1, 0, 1)$

2. The quotient of two negative numbers is _____. *(positive, negative, zero)*

3. The reciprocal of a real number is sometimes called its _____ inverse. *(additive, multiplicative, opposite)*

4. $a \div b$ is the same as _____. $\left(b \div a,\ \dfrac{1}{a} \cdot b,\ a \cdot \dfrac{1}{b}\right)$

Write the reciprocal of each number in simplest form.

5. $\dfrac{3}{5}$ _____   6. 11 _____   7. $-\dfrac{1}{3}$ _____   8. 0.4 _____

Simplify each expression.

9. $\left(-\dfrac{1}{9}\right)(9)$ _____

10. $\dfrac{1}{5}(-35)$ _____

11. $\dfrac{1}{6}(54)$ _____

12. $\dfrac{1}{3}(15a - 21b)$ _____

13. $-\dfrac{1}{9}(-9a + 9)$ _____

14. $(17a - 34b)\left(\dfrac{1}{17}\right)$ _____

15. $212 \div 53$ _____

16. $\dfrac{625a}{25}$ _____

17. $0 \div (-27)$ _____

18. $-11 \cdot \dfrac{a}{11}$ _____

19. $\dfrac{1}{\frac{1}{3}}$ _____

20. $\dfrac{-21}{\frac{1}{7}}$ _____

Evaluate each expression if $a = -2$, $b = 4$, and $c = -5$.

21. $\dfrac{abc}{8}$ _____

22. $\dfrac{b(a + c)}{3 + a}$ _____

23. $(a + 2c)\dfrac{1}{b}$ _____

24. $-\dfrac{1}{3}(a + b + c)$ _____

NAME _____ DATE _____ SCORE _____

Transforming Equations (For use after Section 3–3)

Select each answer from the choices in parentheses. Write the answer in the blank.

1. Equations having the same solution set are called _____. *(equivalent, transformed)*

2. If a, b, and c are any real numbers and $a = b$, then $a + c = $ _____.
(ac, a + b, b + c)

3. If a, b, and c are any real numbers and $a = b$, then $ac = $ _____. *(a + c, bc, ab)*

4. Division "undoes" _____. *(addition, subtraction, multiplication)*

Solve.

5. $a - 12 = 3$ _____

6. $y + 4 = 11$ _____

7. $-6 + x = 4$ _____

8. $-x + 3 = 2$ _____

9. $13 = -t + 5$ _____

10. $m - 3 = |3 - 11|$ _____

11. $-5 + (1 + p) = 4$ _____

12. $4 - (x - 3) = 1$ _____

13. $17b = 34$ _____

14. $35m = 140$ _____

15. $-16 = \dfrac{x}{3}$ _____

16. $15 = -\dfrac{t}{6}$ _____

17. $-23m = -184$ _____

18. $\dfrac{1}{5}x = 13$ _____

19. $-\dfrac{1}{8}q = 3$ _____

20. $65 = -13m$ _____

21. $\frac{1}{3}x = 1\frac{2}{3}$ _____

22. $\dfrac{x}{3} + 6 = 21$ _____

23. $\dfrac{a}{4} - 3 = 2$ _____

24. $-\dfrac{2}{3}(x - 5) = 6$ _____

25. $x + 2 - 3x = 4$ _____

26. $b - (5 - 3b) + (b - 1) = -6$ _____

27. $5(a - 4) + 2 = -8$ _____

28. $6 - \dfrac{2}{3}(15x - 9) = 0$ _____

Solving Problems; Equations Having the Variable in Both Sides (For use after Section 3–5)

Select each answer from the choices in parentheses. Write the answer in the blank.

1. An equation that is true for every value of the variable(s) is called an _____. *(identity, impossibility)*

2. If x is an integer, then the next two consecutive integers are _____. *(2x and 3x, x + 1 and x + 2)*

Solve. If an equation is an identity or if it has no roots, state that fact.

3. $6w + 8w = 15 + 9w$ _____

4. $5 + 3d = 13 - 5d$ _____

5. $6x + 28 = 8x$ _____

6. $9 = 6a + 21$ _____

7. $110 + 11y = 0$ _____

8. $4(5 + 2x) = 4x$ _____

9. $-5 + 2(x + 4) = 3 + 2x$ _____

10. $2f - 6f = 8 - 4f$ _____

11. $5 + 2(x - 4) = 4 + 2x$ _____

12. $10(2 + x) = -5(2x - 4)$ _____

13. $28 + 6z = 16$ _____

14. $5 + |t| = 3$ _____

15. $2y + 7 = 3(y + 6)$ _____

16. $4s + 51 + 6s = 17 + 8s$ _____

17. $0.03(x - 15) = 0.6$ _____

18. $\dfrac{2}{3}x + 4 = 4 + \dfrac{2}{3}x$ _____

Use an equation to solve each problem.

19. Two integers differ by 12. Three times the smaller one is 11 less than twice the larger one. What are the numbers? _____

20. The perimeter of a rectangle is 56 and its length is 8 more than its width. Find the length and width. _____

21. The sum of three consecutive integers is 13 less than four times the smallest. What are the integers? _____

Using Charts; Cost and Value Problems; Proof

(For use after Section 3–8)

Solve.

1. Yolanda is one fourth as old as her mother. Six years ago the sum of their ages was 48. How old is each now?   _____

2. Mario is 6 and his father is 34. How long will it be before his father is three times as old as Mario?   _____

3. Alex is five times as old as Jim, but in twelve years he will only be three times as old. How old is each now?   _____

4. The length of a rectangle is 5 cm more than its width. What are its dimensions if its perimeter is 90 cm?   _____

5. Sheila has a total of 32 nickels and dimes worth $2.15. How many nickels does she have?   _____

6. Goldfish cost $2 and tropical fish cost $2.50. Howard bought three more goldfish than tropical fish and spent $15. How many goldfish did he buy?   _____

Write the missing reasons. Assume that each variable represents any real number.

7. Prove: If $a + b = 0$, then $a = -b$.

Proof: (1) $a + b = 0$ (1) _____

      (2) $(a + b) + (-b) = 0 + (-b)$ (2) _____

      (3) $a + [b + (-b)] = 0 + (-b)$ (3) _____

      (4) $a + 0 = 0 + (-b)$ (4) _____

      (5) $a = -b$ (5) _____

ALGEBRA, Structure and Method, Book 1

Cumulative Review—Chapters 1–3

Simplify.

1. $|9| - |-3|$ _____

2. $18 \div 3(6 - 5)$ _____

3. $12 - (7 - 3)$ _____

4. $3 + 4(5 + 6)$ _____

5. $-31 - 4 + 12 - 6$ _____

6. $-3(a - b) + 5b$ _____

7. $-3(33)\left(\dfrac{1}{3}\right)\left(-\dfrac{1}{11}\right)$ _____

8. $2\frac{2}{3} - 3\frac{1}{3} - 3\frac{1}{3}$ _____

9. $6x - (3 - x)$ _____

10. $6x - (x - 3)$ _____

Evaluate each expression if $a - 5$, $b = -3$, and $c = -2$.

11. $a + b - c$ _____

12. $a - b - |c|$ _____

13. $a(b - c)$ _____

14. $a - (b - c)$ _____

Evaluate each expression if $x = \dfrac{1}{2}$, $y = 0$, and $z = -1$.

15. xyz _____

16. $z - 2x$ _____

17. $\dfrac{xy}{x - z}$ _____

18. $\dfrac{z - 2}{x}$ _____

Solve.

19. $12 + x = -4$ _____

20. $2y = 19$ _____

21. $\dfrac{-r}{6} = -9$ _____

22. $|x| - 4 = -2$ _____

23. $2x - (3 + x) = 8$ _____

24. $2x - (3 - x) = 8$ _____

Solve. If an equation is an identity or has no root, state that fact.

25. $9 + 3y = 21$ _____

26. $9 - 3y = 21$ _____

27. $3m + 4 = 4m - 6$ _____

28. $-32 + 4r = 18 - 6r$ _____

29. $n - 5 = -(5 - n)$ _____

30. $\dfrac{2}{5}x = -30$ _____

31. $3(y + 8) = 2\left(10 + \dfrac{3}{2}y\right)$ _____

32. $18 = 6 - 1.5y$ _____

(continued)

Cumulative Review—Chapters 1–3 (continued)

Write the given numbers in order from least to greatest.

33. $5, -6, -6\frac{1}{2}, \frac{5}{2}$ _____

34. $-1\frac{1}{2}, 0, -2, \frac{3}{4}$ _____

Find the average of each list of numbers.

35. 12, 92, 17, 51 _____

36. -12, 92, -17, 51 _____

Solve.

37. Seven more than a number is 3. Find the number.   _____

38. Six less than twice a number is 10. Find the number.   _____

39. The length of a rectangle is 1 m more than twice its width. What is the length of the rectangle if its perimeter is 110 m?   _____

40. Find two consecutive odd integers whose sum is 76.   _____

41. A baseball team played 109 games. It lost five more games than it won. How many games did it win?   _____

42. Fred has three times as many dimes as quarters. How many dimes does he have if the value of all of the coins is $3.85?   _____

ALGEBRA, Structure and Method, Book 1

Exponents; Adding and Subtracting Polynomials

(For use after Section 4–2)

Select each answer from the choices in parentheses. Write the answer in the blank.

1. In $5x^2$, 5 is called the _____. *(base, variable, coefficient)*

2. In b^n, b is called the _____. *(base, exponent, power)*

3. $9x + 5$ is a _____. *(monomial, binomial, trinomial)*

4. The degree of $8x^2y^3$ is _____. *(2, 3, 5)*

5. The degree of $8x^2 + x^3$ is _____. *(2, 3, 5)*

Write each expression in exponential form.

6. $a \cdot a \cdot a$ _____

7. $2 \cdot x \cdot x \cdot 2$ _____

8. $(-3)(x)(x)(x)(x)$ _____

9. The fifth power of twice y _____

10. The square of negative t _____

Simplify.

11. $-5^2(2^3)$ _____

12. $(-5)^2(1)^3$ _____

13. $8(9 - 3)^2$ _____

14. $(-3 \cdot 4)^2$ _____

15. $-(3 \cdot 4)^2$ _____

16. $(5 \cdot 4 - 8)^2$ _____

Evaluate if $x = 3$ and $y = -4$.

17. $(x + y)^2$ _____

18. $x^3 + y^3$ _____

19. $\left(\dfrac{5y}{x + 2}\right)^2$ _____

Add.

20. $9x + 3$
  $\underline{5x - 4}$

21. $5c^2 + 3cd - d^2$
  $\underline{c^2 - 2cd - d^2}$

22. $3x - 4y + xy$
  $y - xy$
  $\underline{5x - 3y}$

Subtract the lower polynomial from the one above it.

23. $9n - 1$
  $\underline{n - 5}$

24. $5x - y - 12$
  $\underline{-x + y - 10}$

25. $3x^2 - 5x - 1$
  $\underline{5x^2 - 5x + 1}$

Simplify.

26. $(9n^2 + 1) - (5 - 7n^2)$ _____

27. $(x^3 - 5x^2 + x) + (x - x^2)$ _____

Solve.

28. $2n - (3n + 2) = 6$ _____

29. $(2n + 1) - (4 - 6n) = 4n$ _____

Multiplying Monomials; Powers of Monomials

(For use after Section 4–4)

Select each answer from the choices in parentheses. Write the answer in the blank.

1. For all positive integers m and n, $a^m \cdot a^n =$ _____. $(a^{mn},\ a^{m+n},\ a^{m-n})$

2. For all positive integers m and n, $(a^m)^n =$ _____. $(a^{mn},\ a^{m+n},\ a^{m-n})$

Simplify.

3. $c^5 \cdot c^6 \cdot c$ _____

4. $(3y^4)(-3y^4)$ _____

5. $(5x^2)(6x^6)$ _____

6. $(5x^5)^5$ _____

7. $3y^4 \cdot 3y^5$ _____

8. $5(x^5)^5$ _____

9. $\left(\dfrac{3}{4}a\right)\left(\dfrac{4}{3}a\right)(4a)(3a)$ _____

10. $(5x^5)(5x^5)$ _____

11. $(-5m^2)(-6m^2)(-7m^2)$ _____

12. $(2y)^3(2y)^4$ _____

13. $(5x^3)^2$ _____

14. $-(6k^3)^2$ _____

15. $(5x^2)^3$ _____

16. $(xy)^4$ _____

17. $a(a^2)(a^3) - (3a)(3a^2)(3a^3)$ _____

18. $(x^2y)^4$ _____

19. $(4c^2)(3c^3) + (2c^4)(c)$ _____

20. $(x^3y^2)^4$ _____

21. $(4c^2)(3c^3) - (-2c^4)(c)$ _____

22. $5(a^2)^4$ _____

Evaluate if $a = 2$ and $b = -1$.

23. a^2b _____

24. $(ab^3)^2$ _____

25. $-ab^2$ _____

26. $(-ab)^2$ _____

Multiplying Monomials and Polynomials (For use after Section 4–6)

Multiply.

1. $3x(x^2 - 4x - 1)$ _____

2. $-5y^2(3 - y)$ _____

3. $\dfrac{1}{2}a(4a^2 - 2a + 2)$ _____

4. $x^2y(x^2y - xy + y^3)$ _____

Simplify.

5. $2(x + 3) - 3(x + 4)$ _____

6. $3(x - 5) - 5(x - 3)$ _____

7. $-[4x - 3(2 - x)]$ _____

8. $2x^2(x - 5) - (3 - x)x^2$ _____

Solve.

9. $2 + 3(x + 4) = 8$ _____

10. $6 = 2(x + 3) + 3(x + 4)$ _____

11. $5 - 3(x - 1) = 2$ _____

12. $\dfrac{3}{5}(15y - 5) = 2(3 - y)$ _____

Multiply. Use the horizontal form.

13. $(x - 6)(x - 7)$ _____

14. $(x + 6)(x + 7)$ _____

15. $(3t - 2)(t + 4)$ _____

16. $(2c + 3)(2c - 5)$ _____

Multiply. Use the vertical form.

17. $3x - 5$
$\underline{x + 7}$

18. $-x + 3$
$\underline{2x - 6}$

19. $a^2 - 4a - 2$
$\underline{2a + 1}$

20. $5x^2 - 2x + 4$
$\underline{3x^2 + x}$

21. $5c - 8d$
$\underline{4c + 2d}$

22. $3x^2 + 2xy - y^2$
$\underline{5x - 2y}$

Multiply using either the horizontal or the vertical form.

23. $(a - b)(a^2 + ab + b^2)$ _____

24. $(3n + 2)(5 - 4n + 3n^2)$ _____

Solve.

25. $(x + 1)(x - 1) = x^2 + x$ _____

26. $(x - 1)(x - 3) = (x - 2)(x + 4)$ _____

Formulas; Distance-Rate-Time Problems

(For use after Section 4–8)

Solve for the variable indicated. State the restrictions, if any, for the formula obtained to be meaningful.

1. $A = \dfrac{1}{2}bh$; $h =$ _____

2. $I = prt$; $t =$ _____

3. $F = \dfrac{9}{5}C + 32$; $C =$ _____

4. $S = \dfrac{n}{2}(a + 50)$; $n =$ _____

Solve.

5. Two planes 1350 miles apart are flying toward each other at different assigned altitudes. If one is flying at 250 mph and the other at 290 mph, how long will it take them to pass each other? _____

6. If you average 30 mph, a drive between two cities will take 2 hours longer than if you average 35 mph. How far apart are the two cities? _____

7. Two bike riders left each other and started to ride in opposite directions. Two hours later they were 54 miles apart. If one of them averaged twice the average rate of the other, what was the rate of each? _____

8. Cheryl left home on a business trip in her car and averaged 50 mph. The next day she started to return at an average rate of 38 mph. After driving 2 hours longer than she spent on her outward trip, she discovered that she was still 14 miles from home. How far from home had she traveled? _____

9. Two runners can average 8 and 10 yards per second respectively. If the slower runner was given a $7\frac{1}{2}$ second head start in a race that ended in a tie, what was the distance that they raced? _____

ALGEBRA, Structure and Method, Book 1

Area Problems; Problems without Solutions (For use after Section 4–10)

Solve. If a problem has no solution, explain why.

1. A rectangle is 6 cm longer than it is wide. If the length and the width are both increased by 3 cm, the area is increased by 99 cm². Find the original dimensions.

   _____

2. A tinsmith has two pieces of sheet metal with the same area. One is a square and the other is a rectangle 18 cm longer than the square but 9 cm less wide than the square. Find the total area of each piece of metal.

   _____

3. A rectangular garden is 10 m longer than it is wide. The owner wants to increase the size of the garden. If he adds an additional 3 m to each of the four sides, he will gain an additional 216 m² of garden area. What are the dimensions of the original garden?

   _____

4. Sven has three times as many dimes as quarters. His dimes and quarters total $6. How many of each type of coin does he have?

   _____

5. Find two consecutive odd integers whose sum is 65.

   _____

6. Joyce is 5 years older than Laura. In 5 years Joyce will be twice as old as Laura. How old is each now?

   _____

7. Riva's father drives to work each morning at an average rate of 50 mph. Coming home the traffic is heavier, and he averages only 40 mph. His place of work is 20 miles from where Riva's family lives. What is the father's average rate of speed for the daily round trip?

   _____

8. Jasmine has $2.20 in coins, all nickels, dimes, and quarters. If she has twice as many nickels as dimes, how many of each type of coin does she have?

   _____

Factoring Integers; Dividing Monomials; Monomial Factors of Polynomials (For use after Section 5–3)

List all the pairs of integral factors of each integer.

1. 16 _____

2. 43 _____

Give the prime factorization of each number.

3. 100 _____   **4.** 450 _____

5. 243 _____   **6.** 288 _____

Give the GCF of each group of numbers.

7. 75, 105 _____   **8.** 96, 160 _____   **9.** 36, 96, 132 _____

Simplify each expression, assuming that no denominator equals zero.

10. $\dfrac{15a^3b^4}{12a^2b^5}$ _____   **11.** $\dfrac{12r^2st^3}{4r^3st^2}$ _____   **12.** $\dfrac{(-y)^6}{-y^6}$ _____

Find the missing factor.

13. $27x^5y = (3x^3)(\underline{\ ?\ })$ _____   **14.** $-15ab^3c^2 = (5b^3)(\underline{\ ?\ })$ _____

15. $(a^2b^4)^3 = (ab^{10})(\underline{\ ?\ })$ _____   **16.** $(5xy)^5 = (5x)^4(\underline{\ ?\ })$ _____

Divide. Assume that no denominator equals zero.

17. $\dfrac{3x^3 + 6x^2 - 9x}{3x}$ _____   **18.** $\dfrac{6x^2 + 7x}{x}$ _____

19. $\dfrac{y^4 - y^5 - y^7}{y^3}$ _____   **20.** $\dfrac{36x^5y^3 - 12x^6y^5}{12x^5y^3}$ _____

Express each polynomial as the product of its greatest monomial factor and another polynomial.

21. $9x^2 - 15x$ _____   **22.** $5x^3 - 10x^2 + 5x$ _____

Simplify.

23. $\dfrac{4x - 6}{2} + \dfrac{9x - 3}{3}$ _____   **24.** $\dfrac{a^3b^2 - a^2b^3}{a^2b^2} - \dfrac{a^2b - ab^2}{ab}$ _____

Multiplying Binomials; Differences of Squares; Squares of Binomials (For use after Section 5–6)

Write each product as a trinomial.

1. $(x + 6)(x + 4)$ _____

2. $(2c - 3)(3c - 8)$ _____

3. $(y - 6)(y + 4)$ _____

4. $(x - 7)(x + 2)$ _____

5. $2x(x + 1)(x + 2)$ _____

6. $(3x + 5y)(2x - 3y)$ _____

Solve and check.

7. $(x - 3)(x - 2) = (x + 1)(x - 3)$ _____

8. $(x + 4)(x + 5) = (x - 3)(x - 2)$ _____

Express each product as a binomial.

9. $(x - 7)(x + 7)$ _____

10. $(3x - 4)(3x + 4)$ _____

11. $(2c - 5)(2c + 5)$ _____

12. $(a^2 + 2b^2)(a^2 - 2b^2)$ _____

Factor. Use a table of squares.

13. $169 - 4b^2$ _____

14. $625a^4 - 144b^2$ _____

15. $x^6 - 196$ _____

16. $121x^2 - y^2$ _____

Express each square as a trinomial.

17. $(2a - b)^2$ _____

18. $(y^2 + 5)^2$ _____

19. $(3k - 2m)^2$ _____

20. $(3a + 3b)^2$ _____

21. $(x^2 - y^2)^2$ _____

22. $(x^2 + y^2)^2$ _____

Factor each trinomial as the square of a binomial. If it is not possible, write "not factorable."

23. $x^2 - 8x + 16$ _____

24. $4a^2 - 4ab + b^2$ _____

25. $x^2 + 5x + 25$ _____

26. $9a^2 - 12ab + 4b^2$ _____

Factor completely.

27. $12x^2 + 36xy + 27y^2$ _____

28. $a^5 - 2a^4 + a^3$ _____

Factoring $x^2 + bx + c$ and $ax^2 + bx + c$

(For use after Section 5–9)

Factor. Check by multiplying the factors. If the polynomial is not factorable, write "prime."

1. $y^2 - 13y + 12$ _____

2. $x^2 + 7x - 18$ _____

3. $y^2 - 7y + 12$ _____

4. $j^2 - 7j + 10$ _____

5. $y^2 - 8y + 12$ _____

6. $5c^2 + 4c - 1$ _____

7. $y^2 - 11y - 12$ _____

8. $r^2 + 16r + 28$ _____

9. $y^2 - 4y - 12$ _____

10. $y^2 + 12y + 36$ _____

11. $y^2 - y - 12$ _____

12. $h^2 - 12h + 27$ _____

13. $x^2 - 4x + 3$ _____

14. $a^2 + 4a - 32$ _____

15. $2y^2 + y - 3$ _____

16. $1 + 8d + 7d^2$ _____

17. $w^2 + 14w + 33$ _____

18. $d^2 - 2d + 1$ _____

19. $r^2 - 13r + 22$ _____

20. $g^2 + 7g + 49$ _____

21. $p^2 - 12p + 11$ _____

22. $b^2 + 6b - 91$ _____

23. $36y^2 + 13y - 40$ _____

24. $f^2 - 10f + 16$ _____

25. $3x^2 - 11x + 6$ _____

26. $2x^2 - 9x - 35$ _____

27. $b^2 + 14b + 45$ _____

28. $n^2 + 19n + 48$ _____

29. $a^2 + 24a + 23$ _____

30. $9x^2 + 3x - 2$ _____

ALGEBRA, Structure and Method, Book 1

Factoring by Grouping; Using More than One Method of Factoring (For use after Section 5–11)

Factor. Check by multiplying the factors.

1. $7(x + 4) + 3(x + 4)$ _____

2. $5(y + 3) - (y + 3)$ _____

3. $5(y + 3) - y - 3$ _____

4. $ab - 2b + ac - 2c$ _____

5. $x^2 + xy + x + y$ _____

6. $a(b - c) + d(c - b)$ _____

7. $2ac - 6bc - 3a + 9b$ _____

8. $8x^2 - 6xy + 4xz - 3yz$ _____

9. $4x^2 + 8xy - x - 2y$ _____

10. $3(x + 4) - 5(4 + x) - (x + 4)$ _____

Factor each expression as a difference of two squares.

11. $x^2 - (y - 3)^2$ _____

12. $(a - b)^2 - c^2$ _____

13. $25a^2 - (a + 5)^2$ _____

14. $9a^2 - b^2 - 4b - 4$ _____

Factor completely.

15. $5c^2 - 40c - 100$ _____

16. $x^4 - 81$ _____

17. $8x^2 - 8$ _____

18. $x^2y^2 - x^2$ _____

19. $3x^2 + 30x + 72$ _____

20. $36x^2 - 84xy + 49y^2$ _____

21. $x^3 - 144x$ _____

22. $2x^2 + 10x - 1500$ _____

23. $4x^2 - 8x + 4$ _____

24. $a^3 + a^2 - a - 1$ _____

25. $x^3 - 7x^2 + 12x$ _____

26. $x^4 - 6x^2 + 9$ _____

27. $2y^2 - 60y + 450$ _____

28. $10t^2 - 15t - 25$ _____

Solving Equations and Problems by Factoring

(For use after Section 5–13)

Select each answer from the choices in parentheses. Write the answer in the blank.

1. The zero-product property states that if $ab = 0$, then _____ $= 0$.   *(a, b, a or b)*

2. $ax + b = 0$ is a _____ equation.   *(linear, quadratic, cubic)*

3. $ax^2 + bx + c = 0$ is a _____ equation.   *(linear, quadratic, cubic)*

Solve.

4. $(x + 8)(x + 2) = 0$ _____

5. $x^2 - 8x + 12 = 0$ _____

6. $y^2 = 49$ _____

7. $y^2 - 4y = 21$ _____

8. $x(2x - 11) = 0$ _____

9. $y^2 - 2y - 15 = 0$ _____

10. $4y^2 - 9 = 0$ _____

11. $p^2 = 2p$ _____

12. $(2x + 7)(x - 3) = 0$ _____

13. $6x^2 + x = 0$ _____

14. $p^2 - 7p - 60 = 0$ _____

15. $x^3 + 7x^2 - 60x = 0$ _____

16. $2x^2 - 7x - 15 = 0$ _____

17. $(x + 1)(x + 2)(x - 3) = 0$ _____

18. $2x^2 - 5x = 12$ _____

19. $2x^2 - 12 = -5x$ _____

20. $10a^2 - 43a + 45 = 0$ _____

21. $2(x^2 + 5) = 9x$ _____

22. $5m^2 = 5$ _____

23. $(x + 2)(x - 3) = 24$ _____

24. When a positive number is added to its square, the sum is 240. Find the number. _____

25. The sum of the squares of two positive consecutive odd integers is 290. Find the integers. _____

26. The length and width of a rectangle are consecutive integers. If the area of the rectangle is 90 cm^2, what is the perimeter of the rectangle? _____

ALGEBRA, Structure and Method, Book 1

Simplifying and Multiplying Fractions (For use after Section 6–2)

Select each answer from the choices in parentheses. Write the answer in the blank.

1. An algebraic fraction is in simplest form if the _____ of the numerator and denominator is 1 or -1.   *(greatest common factor, least common multiple)*

2. Variables in an algebraic fraction must be restricted so that the _____ does not equal zero.   *(numerator, denominator)*

Express in simplest form, noting any restrictions on the variable.

3. $\dfrac{a - b}{b - a}$ _____

4. $\dfrac{7x - 21}{x - 3}$ _____

5. $\dfrac{y^2 + 8y + 16}{y^2 - 16}$ _____

6. $\dfrac{xy + x}{y^2 + 3y + 2}$ _____

7. $\dfrac{(a - 3)^2}{3 - a}$ _____

8. $\dfrac{x^2 + 2x - 15}{x^2 - 8x + 15}$ _____

9. $\dfrac{(3y - 4)^2}{(4 - 3y)^2}$ _____

10. $\dfrac{6x^2 - 11x + 3}{6x - 9}$ _____

Express each product as a fraction in simplest form.

11. $\dfrac{3}{11} \cdot \dfrac{121}{9}$ _____

12. $\dfrac{bc}{ad} \cdot \dfrac{ac}{bd}$ _____

13. $\dfrac{3x}{y^2} \cdot \dfrac{5y^3}{3x^2}$ _____

14. $\dfrac{6x^3}{5y^3} \cdot \dfrac{20yz}{21x}$ _____

Simplify, using the rules of exponents for the power of a product and the power of a quotient.

15. $(3ab^2)^3$ _____

16. $\left(\dfrac{2x}{y}\right)^2$ _____

17. $\left(\dfrac{5a^2}{c}\right)^3 \cdot \dfrac{2cd}{a^3}$ _____

18. $\dfrac{t^2 - 4t}{t + 2} \cdot \dfrac{t^2 - 4}{2t - 8}$ _____

19. Find the area of a square if each side has length $\dfrac{5x}{3}$ cm. _____

Dividing Fractions; Least Common Denominators

(For use after Section 6–4)

Select each answer from the choices in parentheses. Write the answer in the blank.

1. $\dfrac{a}{b} \div \dfrac{c}{d} = $ _____. $\left(\dfrac{a}{b} \times cd, \ \dfrac{a}{b} \cdot \dfrac{d}{c}, \ \dfrac{ac}{bd} \right)$

2. If $c \neq 0$, $\dfrac{cx}{cy} = $ _____. $\left(\dfrac{x}{y}, \ \dfrac{y}{x}, \ xy \right)$

3. To find the least common denominator of several fractions, you must find the least common

   _____ of the denominators.   (factor, divisor, multiple)

Divide. Express the answers in simplest form.

4. $\dfrac{5}{7} \div \dfrac{3}{14}$ _____

5. $\dfrac{a}{9} \div \dfrac{a}{6}$ _____

6. $\dfrac{5a}{3b^2} \div \dfrac{a^2}{6b^3}$ _____

7. $\dfrac{x^2 - 16}{8} \div \dfrac{2x - 8}{16}$ _____

8. $\dfrac{x^2 - 3x}{9 - x^2} \div \dfrac{x}{3 + x}$ _____

9. $\dfrac{y^2 - 2y - 3}{y^2 - 4y + 3} \div \dfrac{y^2 - 1}{y^2 - 9}$ _____

Simplify.

10. $\dfrac{3}{5} \div \dfrac{1}{5} \cdot \dfrac{2}{3}$ _____

11. $\dfrac{x - y}{x + 2y} \cdot \dfrac{2y + x}{y + x} \div \dfrac{y - x}{x + y}$ _____

Find the missing numerator.

12. $\dfrac{8}{11} = \dfrac{?}{33}$ _____

13. $\dfrac{2x}{3y^2} = \dfrac{?}{9y^3}$ _____

14. $\dfrac{1}{x - y} = \dfrac{?}{x^2 - y^2}$ _____

Find the LCD for each group of fractions.

15. $\dfrac{1}{2y}, \dfrac{1}{2}, \dfrac{1}{y}$ _____

16. $\dfrac{5}{8}, \dfrac{1}{6}, \dfrac{7}{12}$ _____

17. $\dfrac{1}{ab}, \dfrac{1}{bc}, \dfrac{2}{cd}$ _____

18. $\dfrac{3}{x^2 - 7x + 12}, \dfrac{5}{x^2 + x - 20}$ _____

19. $\dfrac{1}{p^2 - 3p}, \dfrac{8}{3p - 9}$ _____

20. $\dfrac{1}{3 - x}, \dfrac{1}{x - 3}, \dfrac{1}{x^2 - 9}$ _____

ALGEBRA, Structure and Method, Book 1

Adding and Subtracting Fractions; Mixed Expressions

(For use after Section 6–6)

Write TRUE if the statement is always true, and FALSE if it is not always true.

1. $4\frac{2}{3} = 4 + \frac{2}{3}$ _____

2. $\dfrac{a}{d} + \dfrac{b}{d} + \dfrac{c}{d} = \dfrac{a+b+c}{d}$ _____

3. $4\frac{2}{3} = \dfrac{4 \cdot 3 + 2}{3}$ _____

4. $\dfrac{a}{b} + \dfrac{a}{c} + \dfrac{a}{d} = \dfrac{a}{b+c+d}$ _____

5. $a\dfrac{b}{c} = \dfrac{ac+b}{c}$ _____

6. $\dfrac{a}{d} + \dfrac{b}{d} + \dfrac{c}{d} = \dfrac{a+b+c}{3d}$ _____

7. $a + \dfrac{b}{c} = \dfrac{ac+b}{c}$ _____

8. $\dfrac{a-b}{c} = \dfrac{a}{c} - \dfrac{b}{c}$ _____

Simplify.

9. $\dfrac{x}{7} + \dfrac{2x-3}{7}$ _____

10. $\dfrac{4}{y+1} + \dfrac{3}{y}$ _____

11. $\dfrac{x}{7} - \dfrac{2x-3}{7}$ _____

12. $\dfrac{x-3}{6} + \dfrac{x-1}{8}$ _____

13. $\dfrac{x}{x+7} - \dfrac{2x-3}{x+7}$ _____

14. $\dfrac{x-3}{6} - \dfrac{x-1}{8} + \dfrac{x}{12}$ _____

15. $\dfrac{x}{x-7} - \dfrac{7}{7-x}$ _____

16. $\dfrac{x}{7} - \dfrac{3}{7x}$ _____

17. $\dfrac{x}{x+2} + \dfrac{2x-4}{x^2-4}$ _____

18. $\dfrac{7}{x} + \dfrac{x+3}{7}$ _____

19. $\dfrac{x}{x+2} - \dfrac{2x-4}{x^2-4}$ _____

20. $\dfrac{x}{x^2-16} + \dfrac{2}{3x+12}$ _____

21. $\dfrac{5(a-3)}{2} - \dfrac{2(a+2)}{3}$ _____

22. $\dfrac{6x-1}{4} - \dfrac{3(a-2)}{8}$ _____

Write each expression as a fraction in simplest form.

23. $-5\frac{3}{8}$ _____

24. $7 + \dfrac{1}{x}$ _____

25. $\dfrac{x}{y} - 5$ _____

26. $\dfrac{2}{x+7} - 1$ _____

27. $\dfrac{a-b}{3} - \dfrac{b-2a}{2} + \dfrac{3a-5b}{5}$ _____

Polynomial Long Division (For use after Section 6–7)

Divide. Write your answer as a polynomial or mixed expression.

1. $\dfrac{x^2 + 5x + 6}{x + 2}$ _____

2. $\dfrac{4x^2 - 20x + 21}{2x - 7}$ _____

3. $\dfrac{12q^2 + 8q + 1}{6q + 1}$ _____

4. $\dfrac{4x^2 - 20x + 22}{2x - 7}$ _____

5. $\dfrac{x^3 - 7x + 6}{x - 2}$ _____

6. $\dfrac{10x^2 + 47x - 15}{10x - 3}$ _____

7. $\dfrac{2x^2 - 5x + 4}{x + 1}$ _____

8. $\dfrac{10x^2 + 47x - 17}{10x - 3}$ _____

9. $\dfrac{x^3 + 27}{x - 3}$ _____

10. $\dfrac{x^3 + 27}{x + 3}$ _____

11. $\dfrac{x^4 + x^2 - 20}{x - 2}$ _____

12. $\dfrac{63y^2 + 3y + 10}{-7y + 2}$ _____

13. $\dfrac{x^4 - 7x^2 + 6}{x^2 - 1}$ _____

14. $\dfrac{x^3 - 4x^2 - 6x + 5}{x - 5}$ _____

15. $\dfrac{2x^3 - 7x^2 + 4x + 3}{2x + 1}$ _____

16. $\dfrac{2x^3 - 3x^2 - 29x + 60}{x + 4}$ _____

17. $\dfrac{x^3 - 7x + 9}{x - 2}$ _____

18. $\dfrac{x^4 - 3x^3 - x + 3}{x - 3}$ _____

19. $\dfrac{x^3 + 8}{x - 2}$ _____

20. $\dfrac{x^3 + 8}{x + 2}$ _____

21. $\dfrac{x^5 - 1}{x - 1}$ _____

22. $\dfrac{x^3 - 18x^2 + 108x - 216}{x - 6}$ _____

23. The volume of a rectangular solid is $n^3 - n^2 - 9n + 9$. The length of the solid is $n + 3$ and the width is $n - 3$. Find the height. _____

24. Factor $6n^3 + 5n^2 - 66n + 40$ given that $n + 4$ is one of the factors. _____

Cumulative Review—Chapters 4–6

Evaluate if $a = -3$, $b = 4$, and $c = 2$.

1. $(ab)^c$ _____

2. ab^c _____

3. $(a - b)^c$ _____

4. $\left(\dfrac{bc}{abc}\right)^b$ _____

Perform the indicated operations. Express the answers in simplest form. Assume that no denominator is zero.

5. $(8a + 3x) + (-3a - 4x)$ _____

6. $(8a + 3x) - (-3a - 4x)$ _____

7. $(-3xy^2)(4x^2y^2)$ _____

8. $(-3xy^2)^3 \cdot (4xy)^2$ _____

9. $\dfrac{32a^3b^2c}{8abc}$ _____

10. $2ab(a + 5b)$ _____

11. $(2a + b)(a + 5b)$ _____

12. $(x + 3y)(x - 3y)$ _____

13. $(x - 3y)^2$ _____

14. $(10a^2b - 5ab^2 + 20ab) \div 5ab$ _____

Solve. If the equation is an identity or has no solution, state that fact.

15. $4m - 3 = 0$ _____

16. $6 - 3x = 8 + 7x$ _____

17. $4m - 3 = 2(2m - 3)$ _____

18. $2x - 5 = -2(2.5 - x)$ _____

19. $4m - 3 = 10m$ _____

20. $(2y - 3) - (3y + 8) = 9$ _____

21. $y^2 + 11y = -18$ _____

22. $5y^2 - 25y = 0$ _____

23. $y + 11y = -18$ _____

24. $(x + 3)^2 = (x + 3)(x - 2)$ _____

(continued)

Cumulative Review—Chapters 4–6 (continued)

Perform the indicated operations. Express the answers in simplest form. Assume that no denominator is zero.

25. $\dfrac{6a^3b^2}{4a^5b^9} \cdot \dfrac{15a^6b^8}{10a^7b^4}$ _____

26. $\dfrac{x-4}{9} \div \dfrac{16-x^2}{3}$ _____

27. $(7x^2 + 8x + 1) \div (x + 1)$ _____

28. $\dfrac{x+6}{8} \cdot \dfrac{4}{x^2 + 2x - 24}$ _____

29. $\dfrac{1}{10 - 2y} \div \dfrac{1}{3y - 15}$ _____

30. $(x^3 + 1) \div (x - 1)$ _____

31. $\dfrac{11}{4x - 2} - \dfrac{9}{6x - 3}$ _____

32. $\dfrac{1}{1 - y} \div \dfrac{y+1}{y^2 - y}$ _____

33. $\dfrac{-5r}{r^2 + 10r + 25} + \dfrac{5}{r + 5}$ _____

34. $\left(x + \dfrac{1}{x}\right) \div \left(x - \dfrac{1}{x}\right)$ _____

Factor completely.

35. $y^2 + 11y + 18$ _____

36. $6x^2 + 3x + 3$ _____

37. $x^2 - 9y^2$ _____

38. $2x^2 + 11xy + 5y^2$ _____

39. $x^2 - 12x + 36$ _____

40. $12x^2 - 12$ _____

41. $2y^2 + 17y - 9$ _____

42. $2x^2 - 4x - 48$ _____

43. $2a + 2b + ac + bc$ _____

44. $r^3 - 4r + 2r^2 - 8$ _____

Solve.

45. Find two consecutive even integers whose product is 80 more than the square of the smaller number. _____

46. Sally is twice as old as Jon. Eight years ago Sally was three times as old as Jon was. How old is Sally now? _____

47. Ben and Carol own 112 shares of stock. Carol owns 4 more than three times the number of shares Ben owns. How many shares does Carol own? _____

48. Two planes left Seattle at the same time, both traveling due east. One had a rate of 185 mph and the other had a rate of 225 mph. After how many hours were they 220 miles apart? _____

Cumulative Review—Chapters 1–6

Perform the indicated operations.

1. $5a - a$ _____

2. $5a(a + 3 - b)$ _____

3. $(5a + 6) - (4 - 3a)$ _____

4. $(x + 5)(x - 6)$ _____

5. $6 + 3(x - 4)$ _____

6. $(-4m^2n^3p)^2$ _____

7. $(2x - 3)(x - 5)$ _____

8. $(2x - 3)(2x + 3)$ _____

9. $(2x - 3)^2$ _____

10. $x(x + 1)(x + 2)$ _____

Evaluate if $a = -3$, $b = \dfrac{1}{2}$, and $c = 2$.

11. $b(a - c)$ _____

12. $b \cdot |a - c|$ _____

13. $a + 4b - c$ _____

14. $(a + b)$ _____

15. ab _____

16. $\dfrac{a - c}{1 - b}$ _____

Factor completely. If the polynomial cannot be factored, write "prime."

17. $x^2 + 7x + 12$ _____

18. $3x^2 + 21x + 36$ _____

19. $2x^2 + 13x + 15$ _____

20. $4r^2 - 9$ _____

21. $y^2 - y - 30$ _____

22. $x^3 + x^2 - 12x$ _____

23. $4y^2 - 100$ _____

24. $4x^2 - 12x + 7$ _____

25. $xy + 3y + 5x + 15$ _____

26. $x^3 - x + 3x^2 - 3$ _____

(continued)

Cumulative Review—Chapters 1–6 *(continued)*

Express the answers in simplest form. Assume that no denominator is zero.

27. $\dfrac{14x^3y^3}{15x^6y} \div \dfrac{98x^2y}{21x^2y^3}$ _____

28. $\dfrac{c-1}{8} \cdot \dfrac{4}{1-c^2}$ _____

29. $\dfrac{8}{c-1} + \dfrac{4}{c^2-1}$ _____

30. $\dfrac{y^2-5y}{8} \cdot \dfrac{16y}{2y-10}$ _____

31. $(x^2 + 7x + 10) \div (x + 2)$ _____

32. $(x^3 - 8) \div x - 2$ _____

33. $\dfrac{c^2-2c}{6c-2} \div \dfrac{2-c}{1-3c}$ _____

34. $\dfrac{4}{x^2-4x} + \dfrac{1}{4-x}$ _____

35. $\dfrac{5x+7}{x^2+7x+12} - \dfrac{5}{x+3}$ _____

36. $\left(y - \dfrac{2}{y}\right) \div \left(y + \dfrac{2}{y}\right)$ _____

Solve. If an equation is an identity or has no solution, state that fact.

37. $14 + 8x = -26$ _____

38. $14 + 8x = -26 + 3x$ _____

39. $2(x - 3) = 8(3 - x)$ _____

40. $4 - 2(x - 3) = 4x - 2$ _____

41. $\dfrac{2y}{-3} = 12$ _____

42. $9 - x = 16$ _____

43. $|x| + 8 = 2$ _____

44. $8 + \dfrac{3}{4}m = 14$ _____

45. $4x = -16x^2$ _____

46. $(y - 3)(y + 6) = (y - 5)^2$ _____

47. The sum of the measures of two angles is 90°. One angle is 28° larger than the other. Find the measure of each angle. _____

48. The width and length of a rectangle are consecutive integers. The perimeter of the rectangle is 154 cm. Find the width and the length. _____

49. One jet travels 30 mph faster than another jet. Both jets left Atlanta, traveling in opposite directions, at 9:00 A.M. At noon they were 2490 miles apart. Find their rates. _____

50. Find two numbers whose sum is 13 and whose squares total 85. _____

ALGEBRA, Structure and Method, Book 1
Copyright © 1986 by Houghton Mifflin Company. All rights reserved. Printed in U.S.A.

Ratio and Proportion (For use after Section 7–2)

Select each answer from the choices in parentheses. Write the answer in the blank.

1. A ratio is the _____ of two numbers. *(quotient, product, sum)*

2. A proportion is an equation that states that two _____ are equal. *(products, sums, ratios)*

3. In the proportion $\dfrac{a}{b} = \dfrac{c}{d}$, a and d are called the _____. *(means, extremes, opposites)*

4. If $\dfrac{a}{b} = \dfrac{c}{d}$ is true, then _____. *(ab = cd, ad = bc, a + d = b + c)*

State each ratio in simplest form.

5. $48:32$ _____

6. $18:24$ _____

7. $15x:60x$ _____

8. $1 \text{ kg}:100 \text{ g}$ _____

9. $5 \text{ h}:5 \text{ d}$ _____

10. $6 \text{ wk}:1 \text{ yr}$ _____

11. $10 \text{ cm}:5 \text{ mm}$ _____

12. $90\text{¢}:\$12$ _____

13. $2 \text{ m}:25 \text{ cm}$ _____

14. The ratio of rainy days to rainless days during November if there were 12 rainy days. _____

Solve.

15. $\dfrac{5}{x} = \dfrac{6}{7}$ _____

16. $\dfrac{y}{4} = \dfrac{9}{3}$ _____

17. $\dfrac{7}{2} = \dfrac{5x}{3}$ _____

18. $\dfrac{4n}{3} = \dfrac{3n}{10}$ _____

19. $\dfrac{30}{x+1} = \dfrac{10}{x-1}$ _____

20. $\dfrac{6-y}{8} = \dfrac{y+2}{2}$ _____

21. Two numbers have a ratio of $5:6$ and their sum is 44. Find the numbers. _____

22. Two dozen oranges cost \$3.36. How much will five dozen oranges cost? _____

Fractional Equations (For use after Section 7–4)

Solve.

1. $\dfrac{x+1}{2} = 4$ _____

2. $\dfrac{3x}{4} - 1 = \dfrac{x}{3}$ _____

3. $\dfrac{3x}{2} + x = 1$ _____

4. $\dfrac{x-2}{3} = \dfrac{x+1}{4}$ _____

5. $\dfrac{8x}{25} = \dfrac{16}{125}$ _____

6. $2y + \dfrac{y}{3} = \dfrac{y}{4} + 5$ _____

7. $\dfrac{1}{3}(x+6) + \dfrac{1}{6}(9-x) = 1$ _____

8. One fifth of the sum of a number and 2 equals one third of the number. What is the number? _____

9. Two numbers are in the ratio 7:3. One third of their sum is 30. Find the numbers. _____

10. The lengths of the sides of a triangle are consecutive even integers. One fifth of the perimeter is 6 less than the length of the shortest side. Find the perimeter. _____

Solve and check. If the equation has no solution, write "no solution."

11. $\dfrac{1}{8} + \dfrac{1}{10} = \dfrac{1}{x}$ _____

12. $\dfrac{1}{x} + \dfrac{1}{5} = \dfrac{1}{2}$ _____

13. $\dfrac{2}{x} + 4 = \dfrac{2}{x}$ _____

14. $\dfrac{3}{5} - \dfrac{1}{x} + \dfrac{9}{10} = 0$ _____

15. $\dfrac{3}{x} = \dfrac{1}{x+2}$ _____

16. $\dfrac{3}{p-2} - \dfrac{5}{p} = 0$ _____

17. $\dfrac{c-6}{c+3} = \dfrac{4}{5}$ _____

18. $\dfrac{1}{x} + \dfrac{1}{x+1} = 0$ _____

19. $\dfrac{2(x-5)}{3} = \dfrac{2x-3}{3}$ _____

20. $\dfrac{1}{x+4} - \dfrac{2}{x-4} = 0$ _____

21. The sum of the reciprocal of a number and $\dfrac{1}{9}$ is $\dfrac{1}{5}$. What is the number? _____

22. Two numbers differ by 14. If the larger number is divided by the smaller, the quotient is 3 and the remainder is 2. Find the numbers. _____

Percents; Percent Problems (For use after Section 7–6)

Select each answer from the choices in parentheses. Write the answer in the blank.

1. Percent means _____. *(hundreds, hundredths)*

2. To change a decimal to a percent, the decimal should be _____ by 100. *(multiplied, divided)*

3. Percent of discount is found by dividing the decrease in price by the _____ price and multiplying by 100. *(original, new)*

4. Annual simple interest equals principal _____ by annual interest rate. *(multiplied, divided)*

Evaluate.

5. 3% of 600 _____

6. 90% of 60 _____

7. 1.2% of 180 _____

8. 450% of 2 _____

9. What percent of 120 is 18? _____

10. 60 is 12% of what number? _____

11. 8 is 5% of what number? _____

12. What percent of 30 is 75? _____

Solve.

13. $1.06x = 22.26$ _____

14. $0.04x + 0.4x = 3.52$ _____

15. $x + 0.07x = 25.68$ _____

16. $0.04x + 0.05(20 - x) = 0.95$ _____

17. Paul was given a 32% discount on a new stereo. If this saved him $86, what was the original price of the stereo? _____

18. The cost of a restaurant meal, including a 7% tax, was $16.05. What was the price of the meal not including the tax? _____

19. An $85 pair of running shoes is marked down 15%. What is the sale price? _____

20. What is the percent of discount if a shop reduces the price of an item from $80 to $68? _____

21. Tina invested $600, part at 8% interest per year, and the rest at 12% interest per year. At the end of a year, the total interest was $56. How much did she invest at each rate? _____

Mixture and Work Problems (For use after Section 7–8)

Solve.

1. Carlos has $4.30 worth of dimes and quarters. If he has eight more dimes than quarters, how many dimes does he have?

2. One pump can empty a swimming pool in 10 hours. A second pump can empty the same pool in 6 hours. How many *minutes* will it take to empty the pool if both pumps are used at the same time?

3. Two computers working on the same task can complete it in 10 seconds. If one of the computers operating alone can complete that task in 18 seconds, how many seconds will it take the other computer working alone to complete the task?

4. How many liters of pure antifreeze must be added to 30 L of a 60% antifreeze solution to obtain a 75% solution?

5. How many kilograms of a 30% acid solution must be added to 80 kg of a 20% solution to produce a 28% acid solution?

6. How many kilograms of water must be evaporated from 80 kg of a 20% salt solution to produce a 25% salt solution?

7. Wild rice sells for $6 per pound, and plain rice sells for $1 per pound. A grocer wants 10 pounds of a mixture to sell for $2 per pound. How much of each type of rice must be used?

8. Luanne can distribute the company mail in 30 minutes. It takes her new helper 50 minutes to do the same job. If they work together, how long will it take them to distribute the mail?

9. It takes Reggie an average of 3 hours to complete his newspaper route. When his sister helps, it only takes 2 hours working together. How long would it take his sister working alone to deliver the newspapers?

10. If you bike a distance of 10 km at 30 km/h, and then return at 20 km/h, what is your average speed for the entire trip?

ALGEBRA, Structure and Method, Book 1

Scientific Notation; Negative Exponents (For use after Section 7–10)

Select each answer from the choices in parentheses. Write the answer in the blank.

1. A number is written in scientific notation when it is written as the product of a number between 1 and 10, and an integral power of _____. *(1, 10, 100)*

2. Any nonzero number raised to the zero power equals _____. *(0, 1, the number)*

3. If $a \neq 0$ and b is a positive integer, then $a^{-b} =$ _____. $\left(-ba, \dfrac{b}{a}, \dfrac{1}{a^b}\right)$

Rewrite each number in scientific notation.

4. 5,000,000 _____ 5. 5280 _____ 6. 0.0000010 _____

7. 25% _____ 8. 0.00345 _____ 9. 1.5 trillion _____

Rewrite each number without using scientific notation.

10. 3.14×10^3 _____ 11. 9.01×10^6 _____ 12. 3.01×10^{-3} _____

13. 8.6×10^{-3} _____ 14. 5×10^5 _____ 15. 1×10^{-11} _____

Evaluate.

16. 4^{-3} _____ 17. 6^{-2} _____

18. $\dfrac{5^3}{5^{-1}}$ _____ 19. $(3^{-2})^3$ _____

20. $(7^{-3} \cdot 7^4)^{-1}$ _____ 21. $(3^{-3})^{-1}$ _____

22. $(-1)^{-5}$ _____ 23. $(3^{-2} + 3^2)^{-1}$ _____

Simplify. Give answers in terms of positive exponents.

24. $y^{-8} \cdot y^7$ _____ 25. $(3.2 \times 10^8)(5 \times 10^{-5})$ _____

26. $\dfrac{x^{-3}}{x^{-8}}$ _____ 27. $\dfrac{x^{-3}}{x^8}$ _____

28. $\dfrac{x^3}{x^{-8}}$ _____ 29. $\dfrac{x^3}{x^8}$ _____

Equations in Two Variables; Points, Lines, Graphs

(For use after Section 8–2)

Select each answer from the choices in parentheses. Write the answer in the blank.

1. The solution to an equation in two variables is _____. *(a real number, a pair of real numbers)*

2. The y-coordinate of a point is called its _____. *(abscissa, ordinate)*

State whether each ordered pair is a solution of the given equation.

3. $y = 5x - 3$; $(-2, -13)$ _____

4. $2y + 3x - 7 = 0$; $(-3, 8)$ _____

5. $x = 3y - 4$; $(-1, 7)$ _____

6. $2x - 3y = 9$; $(9, 3)$ _____

Solve each equation for y in terms of x.

7. $2x - y = 0$ _____

8. $3y - x - 6 = 0$ _____

State the coordinates of the points.

9. A _____

10. B _____

11. C _____

12. D _____

13. E _____

14. F _____

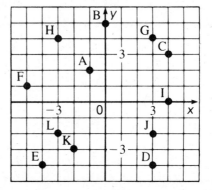

Name the point that is the graph of the ordered pair.

15. $(-3, 4)$ _____

16. $(4, 0)$ _____

17. $(-2, -3)$ _____

18. $(3, -2)$ _____

Graph each equation.

19. $x + y = 2$

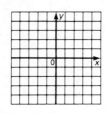

20. $y = \dfrac{1}{2}x + 1$

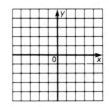

ALGEBRA, Structure and Method, Book 1

The Graphic Method; The Substitution Method

(For use after Section 8–4)

Solve each system by the graphic method.

1. $y = 4 - 3x$
   $y = x - 4$ _____

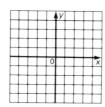

2. $y = x$
   $y = -x + 4$ _____

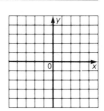

3. $x + y = 0$
   $y = -\dfrac{1}{2}x$ _____

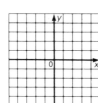

4. $y = 2x$
   $x + 2 = 0$ _____

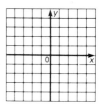

5. $y = x + 1$
   $y + 3 = x$ _____

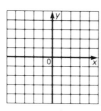

6. $x + y = 3$
   $y = x - 1$ _____

Solve each system by the substitution method. If a system has no solution or an infinite number of solutions, state that fact.

7. $y = 2x - 3$
   $x = 2y - 3$ _____

8. $y = 3x$
   $x + 2y = 21$ _____

9. $y = 3x - 4$
   $2y - 6x = -8$ _____

10. $\dfrac{x}{2} - \dfrac{y}{2} = 3$
   $x + 2y = -3$ _____

11. $x - y = 9$
   $x + y = -5$ _____

12. $-y - 2x = 8$
   $3 - y = 3x$ _____

13. $2x - 3y = 2$
   $x + y = 6$ _____

14. $y = -3x - 2$
   $y + 3x = 5$ _____

Solving Problems with Two Variables; The Addition-or-Subtraction Method (For use after Section 8–7)

Solve, using two equations in two variables.

1. The sum of two numbers is 45. Three times the smaller number exceeds twice the larger number by 5. Find the numbers.   _____

2. Wilma's father is three times as old as she is. Their two ages total 56 years. How old is each?   _____

Solve by the addition-or-subtraction method.

3. $x + y = 10$
   $x - y = 0$ _____

4. $2x + y = 7$
   $2x - 2y = -8$ _____

5. $3a + 2b = 6$
   $4a - 2b = 8$ _____

6. $6x + 4y = 0$
   $6x + y = 9$ _____

Solve by using multiplication with the addition-or-subtraction method.

7. $2x + y = 1$
   $x - 2y = 8$ _____

8. $5x - y = 0$
   $x + 2y = 11$ _____

9. $2x - y = 1$
   $4x - 3y = 5$ _____

10. $2x + y = 5$
    $x + 2y = -2$ _____

Express each equation in standard form. Then solve.

11. $x - y = 4$
    $(x - 6) = 2(y - 6)$ _____

12. $\dfrac{x + 2}{2} = y$

    $\dfrac{x - 2}{3} = 2y$ _____

Solve by whatever method you prefer.

13. $2y - x = -8$
    $3x + 4y = -6$ _____

14. $2x + 3y = 130$
    $x + y = 40$ _____

15. Five years ago, Liz was twice as old as her younger sister. Five years from now, Liz will only be $1\frac{1}{3}$ times as old as her sister. How old is each now?   _____

ALGEBRA, Structure and Method, Book 1
Copyright © 1986 by Houghton Mifflin Company. All rights reserved. Printed in U.S.A.

Wind and Water Current Problems (For use after Section 8–8)

Solve.

1. A boat travels with the current at the rate of 29 km/h and travels against the current at a rate of 21 km/h. What is the rate of the boat in still water? What is the rate of the current?

_____

2. Chris can swim 40 m/min in still water. The West River flows at 5 m/min. How far can Chris swim upstream if his entire swim, upstream and downstream, can take only 20 minutes?

_____

3. The White River flows at 2 mi/h. Phil can paddle his canoe in still water at 8 mi/h. If he is 4 miles downstream from a log floating toward him, how long will it take him to reach the log?

_____

4. A loose boat is floating downstream at 6 km/h. It is 8 km downstream from a power boat trying to catch up to it. If the power boat runs at 20 km/h in still water, how many *minutes* will it take the power boat to overtake the loose boat?

_____

5. In still air a certain plane can fly 800 miles from city A to city B in 4 hours. On a particular day, the same plane took 5 hours to make the same trip. What was the rate of the wind?

_____

6. A 600 mile trip takes 4 hours flying against the wind but only 3 hours flying with the wind. Find the plane's rate in still air and the speed of the wind.

_____

7. A boat takes 7 minutes to go a certain distance upstream, and it can return the same distance in 5 minutes. If the boat's rate in still water is 12 mi/h, what is the rate of the current?

_____

8. An airplane whose speed in still air is 640 km/h can travel 3300 km with the wind in the same amount of time it takes to fly 3100 km against the wind. What is the wind speed?

_____

Digit, Age, and Fraction Problems (For use after Section 8–9)

Solve.

1. The sum of the digits of a two-digit number is 15. If the digits are reversed, the number is increased by 9. What is the original number? _____

2. The sum of the digits of a two-digit number is 8, and their difference is 6. If the value of the number is less than 50, what is the number? _____

3. A number between 100 and 200 is 19 times the sum of its digits. The tens digit is 3 more than the units digit. Find the number. _____

4. Evita's father is three times as old as Evita is. Seven years ago he was five times as old as she was. Find Evita's present age. _____

5. Millie is $\frac{2}{3}$ as old as Maude. Six years from now Millie will be $\frac{5}{7}$ as old as Maude will be. How old is each now? _____

6. The sum of Jim's age and Mike's age is 52. Six years ago Mike was four times as old as Jim was. How old is Jim now? _____

7. The numerator of a fraction is seven more than twice the denominator. The value of the reciprocal of the fraction is 0.4. Find the original fraction. _____

8. The denominator of a fraction is 25 more than the numerator. If the value of the fraction is $\frac{2}{7}$, what is the fraction? _____

9. The numerator of a fraction is 10 less than the denominator. If 2 is subtracted from the numerator and from the denominator, the value of the resulting fraction is $\frac{1}{3}$. Find the original fraction. _____

Slope of a Line (For use after Section 9–1)

Select each answer from the choices given in parentheses. Write the answers in the blanks.

1. The slope of a line = _____ $\left(\dfrac{x_2 - x_1}{y_2 - y_1}, \dfrac{y_2 - y_1}{x_2 - x_1} \right)$

2. Slopes of parallel lines are _____. *(equal, opposites)*

3. Lines with no slope are _____. *(horizontal, vertical)*

Find the slope of the line through the given points.

4. $(9, 5), (7, 6)$ _____

5. $(8, 2), (9, -3)$ _____

6. $(5, 0), (0, 4)$ _____

7. $(8, 3), (-1, -3)$ _____

Find the slope of the line whose equation is given.

8. $2x + y = 4$ _____

9. $x - y = 5$ _____

10. $y = -2x + 4$ _____

11. $2y = 5$ _____

Graph the line through the given point with the given slope.

12. $A = (-3, -2)$
slope $= \dfrac{3}{5}$

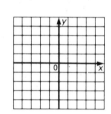

13. $B = (2, -2)$
slope $= -\dfrac{1}{2}$

Solve.

14. Find the value of c if a line with slope $\dfrac{3}{4}$ passes through the points $(1, 8)$ and $(5, c)$. _____

15. Find the value of a if the points $(5, 8)$, $(9, -4)$, and $(a, 2)$ are collinear points. _____

ALGEBRA, Structure and Method, Book 1
     PRACTICE EXERCISES   **107**

The Slope-Intercept Form; Determining an Equation of a Line (For use after Section 9–3)

Match each equation on the left with the correct description on the right. (You will not use all the descriptions.)

1. _____ $y = 3x + 2$ **A.** a linear equation in standard form

2. _____ $3x + 2y = 1$ **B.** a line through the origin

3. _____ $x + 2 = 1$ **C.** one of the axes

4. _____ $3 + y = 0$ **D.** an equation in slope-intercept form

5. _____ $x = y$ **E.** a horizontal line

          F. a vertical line

Write an equation in standard form that has the given slope and y-intercept.

6. $m = 5$, $b = -2$ _____   7. $m = \dfrac{1}{2}$, $b = \dfrac{1}{4}$ _____

Change each equation to slope-intercept form. Then draw the graph, using only the slope and y-intercept.

8. $x + 3y = 6$ 9. $5y = 10x$ 10. $x - y - 1 = 0$

_____   _____   _____

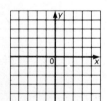   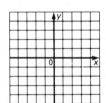

Write an equation in standard form for each line described.

11. The line that passes through the point $(-1, 1)$ and has slope 2.   _____

12. The line through the origin with slope $\dfrac{2}{3}$.   _____

13. The line through $(2, -4)$ and parallel to the graph of $y = 2x - 5$.   _____

14. The line through $(-3, 1)$ having the same y-intercept as the graph of $x - 2y = -4$.   _____

Functions Defined by Equations, Tables, and Graphs

(For use after Section 9–5)

Given the functions $f: x \rightarrow 3x - 4$ and $g: x \rightarrow x^2 + 3$, find the following values of f and g.

1. $f(8)$ _____

2. $g(2)$ _____

3. $f(0)$ _____

4. $f(-5)$ _____

5. $g(-2)$ _____

6. $g(0)$ _____

7. $f\left(\dfrac{1}{2}\right)$ _____

8. $g\left(-\dfrac{1}{2}\right)$ _____

9. $2f(3)$ _____

Find the range of each function.

10. $s: z \rightarrow 2 - 3z$, $D = \{-3, -1, 0, 1, 3\}$. _____

11. $t: x \rightarrow 1 - x^2$, $D = \{-2, -1, 0, 1, 2\}$. _____

Find $f(0)$. Solve $f(x) = 0$.

12. $f(x) = 1 - 3x$ _____

13. $f(x) = x^3 - x^2$ _____

14. Make a bar graph for the function shown in the table.

Eastville	
Month	Low Temp. (F°)
Jan.	16
Feb.	20
Mar.	27
Apr.	36
May	44

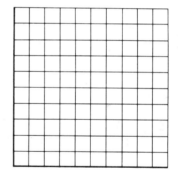

15. Julio kept a record for five days of the distance that he jogged each day. Make a broken-line graph of the function.

Mon.	4.0 km
Tues.	5.0 km
Wed.	8.5 km
Thurs.	7.0 km
Fri.	2.5 km

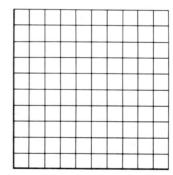

Linear and Quadratic Functions (For use after Section 9–6)

Select each answer from the choices given in parentheses. Write the answer in the blank.

1. A linear function is a function whose graph is a _____. *(line, parabola)*

2. The graph of a quadratic function is a _____. *(line, parabola)*

3. The vertex of the parabola $f(x) = 2x^2 + 3x + 4$ is a _____ point. *(maximum, minimum)*

4. Given $y = ax^2 + bx + c$, if a is negative, the parabola opens _____. *(downward, upward)*

Draw the graph of each function.

5. $f: x \rightarrow 2x + 3$

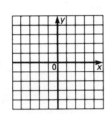

6. $r(x) = -\dfrac{2}{3}x$

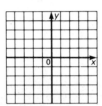

Find the coordinates of the vertex and the equation of the axis of symmetry of the graph of each equation. Use the vertex and at least four other points to graph the equation.

7. $y = x^2 + 3x$

_____

_____

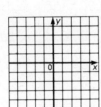

8. $y = 4 - 2x^2$

_____

_____

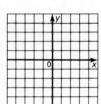

ALGEBRA, Structure and Method, Book 1

Direct, Inverse, Joint, and Combined Variation

(For use after Section 9–10)

Solve.

1. If a varies directly as c, and $a = 108$ when $c = 6$, find a when $c = 30$. _____

2. If m varies inversely as n, and $m = 3$ when $n = 6$, find m when $n = \dfrac{1}{30}$. _____

3. If y is directly proportional to x^2, and $y = 144$ when $x = 4$, find y when $x = 5$. _____

4. If t is inversely proportional to v^2, and $t = 1$ when $v = 5$, find t when $v = 10$. _____

5. The area of a square varies directly as the square of the length of its side. If the length of a side is tripled, how does the area of the resulting square compare with the original square? _____

6. John, who weighs 100 pounds, is on a seesaw with his sister, Mary, who weighs 75 pounds. John sits 4 feet from the seesaw support. How far from the support must Mary sit in order to balance John? _____

7. The volume of a cylindrical can varies jointly as its height and the square of its radius. What is the effect on the volume when the radius of the can is doubled and the height remains the same? _____

8. The number of revolutions made by a wheel varies directly as the distance it rolls and inversely as the radius of the wheel. What is the effect on the number of revolutions of a wheel if it travels the same distance, but its radius is doubled? _____

Cumulative Review—Chapters 7–9

Simplify. Give the answers in terms of positive exponents.

1. $3a^{-2}$ _____

2. $(x^2y^{-3})^2$ _____

Perform the indicated operations. Express the answers in simplest form. Assume that no denominator is zero.

3. $(2x - 5)^2$ _____

4. $\dfrac{d^2 - 3d + 2}{2d + 2} \cdot \dfrac{d + 1}{d - 1}$ _____

5. $\dfrac{x^2 - 1}{1 - x}$ _____

6. $(x + 3)(x^2 - 3x + 9)$ _____

Solve.

7. $\dfrac{c}{c - 4} = \dfrac{4}{5}$ _____

8. $\dfrac{7}{c - 4} = \dfrac{5}{c - 2}$ _____

9. $\dfrac{6}{y + 8} = \dfrac{3}{7}$ _____

10. $y + \dfrac{y + 1}{3} = 0$ _____

11. $\dfrac{r}{3} + \dfrac{r}{2} = 5$ _____

12. $0.08x + 0.04(12 - x) = 4$ _____

13. $\dfrac{2x + 1}{3} = \dfrac{3x - 1}{7}$ _____

14. $\dfrac{1}{y - 1} + \dfrac{y}{10} = \dfrac{y + 1}{2y - 2}$ _____

15. $\dfrac{p}{2} - \dfrac{p - 1}{3} = 2$ _____

16. $\dfrac{1}{8} + \dfrac{1}{14} = \dfrac{1}{x}$ _____

17. $\dfrac{1}{3}(x + 6) + \dfrac{1}{12}(9 - x) = 2$ _____

18. $\dfrac{1}{8} + \dfrac{1}{x} = \dfrac{1}{5}$ _____

19. $x^2 - 9x = -14$ _____

20. $x^2 - 16x = 0$ _____

Solve each system, using whatever method you prefer.

21. $2x + 5y = 12$
$x - 2y = -3$ _____

22. $y = -4x + 5$
$3x - 2y = 12$ _____

23. $2x + 3y = 12$
$2x - y = 4$ _____

24. $3x - 2y = 14$
$2x = -y$ _____

(continued)

Cumulative Review—Chapters 7-9 *(continued)*

Solve.

25. 30% of 80 is what number? _____

26. 90 is 30% of what number? _____

27. What percent of 80 is 30? _____

28. What percent of 120 is 150? _____

29. Express 0.0000268 in scientific notation. _____

30. Find the slope of the line that passes through $(5, -4)$ and $(-1, 8)$. _____

31. Find an equation of the line that passes through $(2, 0)$ and has slope 3. _____

32. Find an equation of the line that passes through $(2, 0)$ and $(4, 8)$. _____

Graph each equation.

33. $y = -2x$

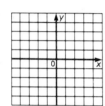

34. $3x + 2y = 6$

35. Given $f(x) = \dfrac{1}{2}x^2 - 1$. Find the least value of the function. _____

Solve.

36. How many jars of nuts worth $4 per jar must be mixed with some nuts worth $6 per jar to get 50 jars of nuts worth $4.80 per jar? _____

37. A department store is having a sale, offering a 15% discount on the regular price of any item. Find the sale price if the regular price of an item is $120. _____

38. The freshman class of 450 students has a boy to girl ratio of $7:8$. How many boys are there? _____

39. Tom and Jon together can wash their car in 12 minutes. It takes Tom 18 minutes to wash the car by himself. How many minutes would it take Jon to wash the car alone? _____

40. Freda has 35 coins valued at $7.15. If she only has nickels and quarters, how many nickels does she have? _____

Order of Real Numbers; Solving Inequalities

(For use after Section 10–2)

Select each answer from the choices in parentheses. Write the answer in the blank.

1. The symbol for "is less than" is _____. $(\leq, <, \geq, >)$

2. The symbol _____ means "is greater than or equal to." $(\leq, <, \geq, >)$

3. Multiplying each side of an inequality by the same real _____ number reverses the order of the inequality. *(positive, negative)*

4. The absolute value of a number is never _____. *(zero, positive, negative)*

Match each inequality with the graph of its solution set. A graph may be used more than once.

5. _____ $-y < -2$

6. _____ $-y \geq 2$

7. _____ $3y > -6$

8. _____ $-3y > -6$

9. _____ $y - 1 > 1$

a.

b.

c.

d.

Solve each inequality and draw its graph.

10. $3r + 5 < 20$ _____

11. $2y + 1 \leq -5y + 8$ _____

12. $8 \leq 2x - 8(x - 1)$ _____

13. $8 - 3(x + 4) < -x - 6$ _____

ALGEBRA, Structure and Method, Book 1

Solving Problems Involving Inequalities

(For use after Section 10–3)

Solve.

1. Find the largest pair of consecutive even integers whose sum is less than 85. _____

2. Eve's grades on three tests were 78, 93, and 63. What is the lowest grade she can get on the next test to have an average higher than 80? _____

3. Carlos has more than 80 coins, all nickels and dimes. He has five more dimes than nickels. What is the least number of nickels that Carlos can have? _____

4. The sum of three consecutive odd integers is less than 327. What is the largest value that the smallest of these three numbers can have? _____

5. Karen Chun spent less than $60 for a skirt and blouse. If the blouse cost $9 more than twice the cost of the skirt, what is the most she could have spent on the skirt? _____

6. Tony is 50 years older than Brett. Twenty years ago Tony was at least three times as old as Brett was. At most, how old is Brett now? _____

7. The length of a rectangle is 3 times as great as its width. If the perimeter of the rectangle is no more than 72 cm, what is the greatest possible length of the rectangle? _____

8. Two trains traveling in opposite directions pass each other on parallel tracks. One train averages at most 80 km/h, and the other averages at most 65 km/h. What is the least possible time that it could take for the two trains to be 290 km apart? _____

9. A vat contains 100 gallons of a 50% brine solution. What is the greatest amount of water that can be added if the salt content cannot drop below 25%? _____

Solving Combined Inequalities (For use after Section 10–4)

Solve each open sentence and graph each solution set that is not empty.

1. $x < 0$ and $-x < 3$ _____

2. $-x > 6$ or $x > 3$ _____

3. $5 < x < 7$ _____

4. $x > 5$ and $x \geq 7$ _____

5. $x \leq 5$ or $x > 7$ _____

6. $x < 5$ or $x < 7$ _____

7. $-5 \geq x > -10$ _____

8. $7 < -x < 8$ _____

9. $2x + 1 \geq 5$ and $x - 8 < 2$ _____

10. $2x > 8$ or $-3x \leq 15$ _____

11. $2 > x + 3 > -8$ _____

12. $1 + 2x > 5$ and $8 - x < 7$ _____

13. $2x + 1 < 7$ or $2x + 1 > -7$ _____

14. $-1 < 2x - 1 < 11$ _____

15. $-14 > 5x + 6 > -4$ _____

16. $2(x - 2) < 4$ or $4 \leq 2(x - 2)$ _____

Absolute Value in Open Sentences (For use after Section 10–6)

Solve each open sentence and graph its solution set.

1. $|x| > 3$ _____

2. $|x| \leq 3$ _____

3. $|x - 2| = 3$ _____

4. $|x - 2| > 3$ _____

5. $|x - 2| < 3$ _____

6. $|2 - x| = 5$ _____

7. $-|x| < -3$ _____

8. $|x + 1| \geq 2$ _____

9. $|x + 3| < 4$ _____

10. $|2x - 1| = 3$ _____

11. $2|x - 1| = 3$ _____

12. $|2x| - 1 = 3$ _____

13. $|5x - 7| \geq 3$ _____

14. $|2x - 1| > 3$ _____

15. $1 - |4 - x| \leq -5$ _____

16. $|3 - (x - 1)| < 5$ _____

Graphing Linear Inequalities; Systems of Linear Inequalities

(For use after Section 10–8)

Graph each inequality.

1. $y \geq -3x + 1$

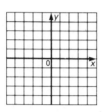

2. $y < \dfrac{x}{2}$

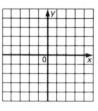

3. $x + 2y \leq 4$

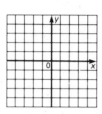

4. $3x - y > 0$

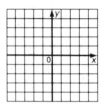

Graph each pair of inequalities and indicate the solution set of the system with crosshatching or shading.

5. $y > 2x - 3$
    $x > 2y - 3$

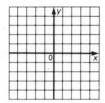

6. $y \leq -x + 3$
    $y \geq x - 4$

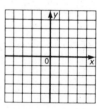

7. $2x + 3y < 3$
    $y > 0$

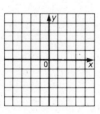

8. $y > x$
    $x - 1 \leq 0$

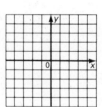

Write a system of linear inequalities whose solution set is shown by the shaded region in each graph.

9. _____

_____

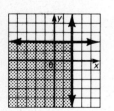

10. _____

_____

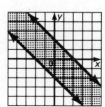

ALGEBRA, Structure and Method, Book 1

Properties and Decimal Forms of Rational Numbers

(For use after Section 11–2)

Select each answer from the choices in parentheses. Write the answer in the blank.

1. If $b \neq 0$ and if a and b are both _____, then $\dfrac{a}{b}$ is called a rational number. *(integers, real numbers)*

2. The _____ property says that between every pair of rational numbers there is another rational number. *(density, closeness)*

3. _____ numbers are sometimes called fractions. *(Rational, Irrational)*

4. _____ fractions can be written as decimals. *(All, Not all)*

Arrange each group of numbers in order from least to greatest.

5. $\dfrac{5}{6}, \dfrac{6}{7}, \dfrac{7}{8}$ _____

6. $\dfrac{32}{34}, \dfrac{33}{34}, \dfrac{31}{34}$ _____

7. $\dfrac{31}{35}, \dfrac{31}{34}, \dfrac{31}{36}$ _____

8. $\dfrac{2}{3}, \dfrac{3}{5}, \dfrac{4}{7}, \dfrac{7}{11}$ _____

Find the number halfway between the given numbers.

9. $\dfrac{3}{5}, \dfrac{5}{6}$ _____

10. $2\tfrac{1}{2}, 5\tfrac{1}{4}$ _____

11. $-\dfrac{3}{25}, -\dfrac{5}{100}$ _____

Express each rational number as a terminating or a repeating decimal.

12. $\dfrac{7}{25}$ _____

13. $\dfrac{5}{7}$ _____

14. $-3\tfrac{1}{8}$ _____

15. $\dfrac{7}{9}$ _____

Express each rational number as a fraction in simplest form.

16. 0.27 _____

17. $0.\overline{25}$ _____

18. $1.1\overline{3}$ _____

Find the difference of the given numbers. Then find the number halfway between them.

19. $\dfrac{1}{2}, \dfrac{1}{3}$ _____

20. $\dfrac{1}{4}, 0.\overline{25}$ _____

Rational and Irrational Square Roots (For use after Section 11–4)

Select each answer from the choices in parentheses. Write the answer in the blank.

1. $\sqrt{a}$ stands for the principal or _____ square root of a. (*negative, nonnegative*)

2. $\sqrt{a} \cdot \sqrt{b}$ _____ $\sqrt{ab}$. (*equals, does not equal*)

3. $\sqrt{a} + \sqrt{b}$ _____ $\sqrt{a + b}$. (*equals, does not equal*)

4. Every real number can be expressed as a _____. (*decimal, fraction*)

Find the indicated square roots.

5. $\sqrt{16}$ _____

6. $\sqrt{625}$ _____

7. $\sqrt{\dfrac{225}{16}}$ _____

8. $\sqrt{17^2}$ _____

9. $\sqrt{\dfrac{121}{4}}$ _____

10. $\sqrt{\dfrac{16}{169}}$ _____

Simplify.

11. $\sqrt{196}$ _____

12. $\sqrt{162}$ _____

13. $\sqrt{50}$ _____

14. $\sqrt{500}$ _____

15. $\sqrt{98}$ _____

16. $\sqrt{63}$ _____

Using a square root table or a calculator, approximate each root to the nearest tenth.

17. $\sqrt{200}$ _____

18. $\sqrt{250}$ _____

19. $\sqrt{5000}$ _____

20. $\sqrt{48}$ _____

21. $\sqrt{700}$ _____

22. $\sqrt{450}$ _____

Between which two consecutive integers does each square root lie?

23. $\sqrt{95}$ _____

24. $\sqrt{250}$ _____

25. $\sqrt{125}$ _____

26. $\sqrt{50}$ _____

ALGEBRA, Structure and Method, Book 1

Square Roots of Variable Expressions; The Pythagorean Theorem (For use after Section 11–6)

Simplify.

1. $\sqrt{y^4}$ _____

2. $\sqrt{x^6}$ _____

3. $\sqrt{t^{10}}$ _____

4. $\sqrt{72x^2}$ _____

5. $\sqrt{121x^2y^6}$ _____

6. $\sqrt{45y^4}$ _____

7. $\sqrt{49y^6}$ _____

8. $\sqrt{169r^{22}}$ _____

9. $\sqrt{9y^8}$ _____

10. $\sqrt{0.49x^2}$ _____

11. $\sqrt{625x^2y^4}$ _____

12. $\sqrt{a^2b^6c^8}$ _____

13. $\sqrt{x^2 + 14x + 49}$ _____

14. $\sqrt{x^2 - 8x + 16}$ _____

Solve.

15. $t^2 = 36$ _____

16. $n^2 - 8100 = 0$ _____

17. $5x^2 - 125 = 0$ _____

18. $49 = 36x^2$ _____

19. $x^2 - 49 = 0$ _____

20. $2m^2 - 128 = 0$ _____

In the following exercises, refer to the right triangle. Find the missing length correct to the nearest hundredth.

21. $a = 4$, $b = 5$, $c = ?$ _____

22. $a = ?$, $b = 1$, $c = \sqrt{7}$ _____

23. $a = 24$, $b = ?$, $c = 30$ _____

24. $a = 2$, $b = 3$, $c = ?$ _____

25. $a = 12$, $b = ?$, $c = 15$ _____

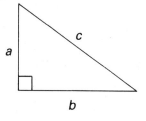

Solve. Approximate irrational answers to the nearest tenth.

26. Find the length of a side of a square whose area is 121 cm². _____

27. Find the length of the diagonal of a square whose area is 9 cm². _____

28. Find the perimeter of a square whose area is 400 square inches. _____

State whether or not the three numbers given could represent the lengths of the sides of a right triangle.

29. 10, 24, 26 _____

30. 3, 6, 9 _____

31. $6a$, $8a$, $10a$ _____

Operations on Radicals (For use after Section 11–8)

Express in simplest form. Assume that all variables represent positive real numbers.

1. $\sqrt{6} \cdot 3\sqrt{6}$ _____

2. $\sqrt{5} \cdot \sqrt{6} \cdot \sqrt{10}$ _____

3. $2\sqrt{3} \cdot \sqrt{6}$ _____

4. $\sqrt{3} \cdot \sqrt{27}$ _____

5. $\sqrt{3} \cdot \sqrt{12} \cdot \sqrt{50}$ _____

6. $\sqrt{5} \cdot \sqrt{\dfrac{3}{5}}$ _____

7. $\sqrt{\dfrac{8}{11}} \cdot \sqrt{\dfrac{11}{8}}$ _____

8. $\sqrt{\dfrac{8}{11}} \cdot \sqrt{22}$ _____

9. $\dfrac{2\sqrt{5}}{\sqrt{50}}$ _____

10. $\dfrac{\sqrt{3}}{\sqrt{18}}$ _____

11. $\dfrac{5\sqrt{45}}{\sqrt{15}}$ _____

12. $\dfrac{3\sqrt{27}}{4\sqrt{3}}$ _____

13. $\sqrt{\dfrac{50}{4}}$ _____

14. $\dfrac{8\sqrt{405}}{\sqrt{5}}$ _____

15. $(3\sqrt{a^2b^3})(-\sqrt{a})$ _____

16. $3x(\sqrt{5x})^2$ _____

17. $8\sqrt{5} - 3\sqrt{5}$ _____

18. $2\sqrt{6} - 3\sqrt{6}$ _____

19. $\dfrac{1}{2}\sqrt{5} + \dfrac{1}{4}\sqrt{20}$ _____

20. $\sqrt{28} - \sqrt{7}$ $2\sqrt{7} - \sqrt{7} = \sqrt{7}$

21. $\sqrt{90} - \sqrt{40}$ $3\sqrt{10} - 2\sqrt{10} = \sqrt{10}$

22. $\sqrt{8} + \sqrt{\dfrac{1}{2}}$ _____

23. $3\sqrt{28} + \sqrt{63}$ _____

24. $\sqrt{75} - 2\sqrt{27} + \sqrt{48}$ _____

25. $3\sqrt{\dfrac{9}{10}} - \sqrt{10}$ _____

26. $\sqrt{x^6} + \sqrt{x^4}$ _____

27. $3\sqrt{2}(\sqrt{8} - \sqrt{32})$ _____

28. $\sqrt{\dfrac{x^2}{a^2} - \dfrac{x^2}{b^2}}$ _____

Multiplication of Binomials Containing Radicals; Radical Equations (For use after Section 11–10)

Express in simplest form.

1. $(\sqrt{3} + 4)(\sqrt{3} - 4)$ _____

2. $(8 - \sqrt{2})(8 + \sqrt{2})$ _____

3. $(\sqrt{5} + \sqrt{6})(\sqrt{5} - \sqrt{6})$ _____

4. $(\sqrt{3} - 4)^2$ _____

5. $(8 + \sqrt{2})^2$ _____

6. $(\sqrt{5} + \sqrt{6})^2$ _____

7. $(2\sqrt{3} + 4)(5\sqrt{7} + 7)$ _____

8. $2\sqrt{3}(5\sqrt{6} - 3)$ _____

Simplify. Rationalize the denominator of each fraction.

9. $\dfrac{5}{\sqrt{3} + 4}$ _____

10. $\dfrac{\sqrt{5}}{\sqrt{3} - 4}$ _____

11. $\dfrac{4}{8 - \sqrt{2}}$ _____

12. $\dfrac{4}{\sqrt{2} - 8}$ _____

13. $\dfrac{6}{2\sqrt{3} + 3}$ _____

14. $\dfrac{2 + \sqrt{5}}{2 - \sqrt{5}}$ _____

Solve.

15. $\sqrt{5a} = 10$ _____

16. $\sqrt{2n} + 3 = 8$ _____

17. $\sqrt{\dfrac{r}{4}} = 5$ _____

18. $\sqrt{\dfrac{4y}{5}} - 4 = 0$ _____

19. $\sqrt{2n + 3} = 8$ _____

20. $\sqrt{\dfrac{2x + 3}{5}} = 3$ _____

21. $\sqrt{4 - 3x} = 5$ _____

22. $-4 = 1 - \sqrt{3 - x}$ _____

23. $2\sqrt{y} = 4\sqrt{5}$ _____

24. $\sqrt{x^2 - 9} = x - 1$ _____

Quadratic Equations with Perfect Squares; Completing the Square (For use after Section 12–2)

Solve. Express irrational solutions in simplest radical form. If the equation has no solution, write "no solution."

1. $x^2 = 36$
2. $a^2 = \dfrac{16}{25}$

3. $5x^2 = 130$
4. $x^2 + 5 = 130$

5. $(x - 3)^2 = 16$
6. $(x + 3)^2 = 16$

7. $(x - 3)^2 = 17$
8. $2(x + 3)^2 = 12$

9. $2(3x + 4)^2 = 20$
10. $2(3x + 4)^2 = -20$

11. $\left(x - \dfrac{3}{4}\right)^2 = \dfrac{1}{2}$
12. $x^2 + 10x + 25 = 6$

Solve by completing the square. Give irrational roots in simplest radical form. If the equation has no solution, write "no solution."

13. $x^2 - 2x = 35$
14. $a^2 + 4a = 5$

15. $q^2 + 5q = 0$
16. $x^2 - 7x + 10 = 0$

17. $x^2 + 7x + 10 = 0$
18. $3a^2 - 8a + 5 = 0$

19. $x^2 - 2x - 4 = 0$
20. $y^2 + 4y = -2$

21. $r^2 - r - 1 = 0$
22. $d^2 + 8d + 10 = 0$

23. $x^2 - 16x = 8$
24. $x^2 - 2x = 5$

25. $y^2 + 3y = 9$
26. $r^2 - 3r = 3$

ALGEBRA, Structure and Method, Book 1

The Quadratic Formula (For use after Section 12–3)

Use the quadratic formula to solve each equation. Give irrational roots in simplest radical form.

1. $2x^2 + x - 3 = 0$ _____

2. $y^2 - y - 12 = 0$ _____

3. $10b^2 + 7b - 12 = 0$ _____

4. $w^2 + 2w = 1$ _____

5. $m^2 - 6m + 3 = 0$ _____

6. $5n^2 + 2n - 3 = 0$ _____

7. $4p^2 + 5p = 0$ _____

8. $3l^2 + l - 5 = 0$ _____

9. $2t^2 + 4t = 1$ _____

10. $5x^2 = 3x$ _____

11. $x^2 + 3x = -1$ _____

12. $t^2 = 31 + t$ _____

13. $x^2 - 5x = -4$ _____

14. $3r^2 - 2r = 4$ _____

15. $x^2 + 8x - 4 = 0$ _____

16. $10t^2 - t - 1 = 0$ _____

Solve, using the quadratic formula.

17. The square of a positive number is 56 more than the number itself. Find the number. _____

18. The sum of a number and 6 times its reciprocal is 5. Find the number. (There are two solutions.) _____

19. Find two consecutive positive even integers whose product is 224. _____

20. Find the dimensions of a rectangular lawn whose perimeter is 100 feet and whose area is 600 square feet. _____

Graphs of Quadratic Equations; The Discriminant

(For use after Section 12–4)

Write the value of the discriminant of each equation. Then use it to decide how many different real-number roots the equation has. (Do not solve.)

Equation	Discriminant	Number of Real Roots
1. $x^2 + 5x + 9 = 0$	_____	_____
2. $2x^2 - 4x - 9 = 0$	_____	_____
3. $5x^2 + x - 3 = 0$	_____	_____
4. $x^2 - x - 6 = 0$	_____	_____
5. $x^2 - x + 6 = 0$	_____	_____
6. $x^2 + 6x + 9 = 0$	_____	_____
7. $x^2 + 4x + 7 = 0$	_____	_____
8. $-x^2 - 2x + 3 = 0$	_____	_____

The graph of each of the following equations is a parabola. Write the answers to the questions about each graph.

Equation	Number of x-Intercepts?	Does the Graph Open Up or Down?	Is the Vertex Above or Below or on the x-Axis?
9. $y = x^2 - x - 6$	_____	_____	_____
10. $y = x^2 - x + 6$	_____	_____	_____
11. $y = x^2 + 6x + 9$	_____	_____	_____
12. $y = x^2 + 4x + 7$	_____	_____	_____
13. $y = -x^2 - 2x + 3$	_____	_____	_____

Graph. Make use of the answers to problems 9 and 13.

14. $y = x^2 - x - 6$
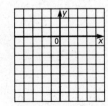

15. $y = -x^2 - 2x + 3$
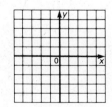

Methods of Solution; Solving Problems Involving Quadratic Equations (For use after Section 12–6)

Solve by the most efficient method. Write irrational answers in simplest radical form.

1. $x^2 + 9x = -20$ _____

2. $x^2 - 9x = -20$ _____

3. $x^2 + 9x = 30$ _____

4. $x^2 - 10x = 30$ _____

5. $5x^2 + 14x - 3 = 0$ _____

6. $5x^2 + 14x = 0$ _____

7. $5y = 10y^2$ _____

8. $x^2 - 29x + 100 = 0$ _____

9. $\dfrac{2}{3}x^2 - \dfrac{1}{3}x - 3 = 0$ _____

10. $(x + 1)^2 - 3(x + 1) = 4$ _____

11. $\dfrac{x + 1}{x - 1} = \dfrac{x - 1}{2x + 1}$ _____

12. $\dfrac{2x}{3} = \dfrac{2}{3x - 1}$ _____

Solve.

13. The sum of a number and its square is 156. Find the number. _____

14. The sum of two numbers is 19, and the sum of their squares is 193. What are the numbers? _____

15. Consuela uses 22 m of fencing to enclose three sides of a rectangular garden. The fourth side is a wall. If the area of the garden is 48 m², find its length and width. _____

16. The width of a rectangular park is 8 m shorter than its length. If the area of the park is 345 m², find the length and the width. _____

17. Working alone, Anton can install a brick patio in 2 hours less than Bill. Together Anton and Bill can install the patio in 4 hours. To the nearest tenth of an hour, how long does it take Bill to install the patio working alone? _____

Cumulative Review—Chapters 10–12

Simplify.

1. $\sqrt{\dfrac{49}{121}}$ _____

2. $\dfrac{3\sqrt{8}}{\sqrt{3}}$ _____

3. $\sqrt{1125}$ _____

4. $\sqrt{33} \cdot \sqrt{\dfrac{9}{11}}$ _____

5. $5\sqrt{21} - \sqrt{21}$ _____

6. $(\sqrt{5} + 3)^2$ _____

7. $(\sqrt{5} + \sqrt{11})(\sqrt{11} - \sqrt{5})$ _____

8. $\sqrt{3}(3\sqrt{2} - 6)$ _____

9. $\sqrt{121x^2}$ _____

10. $-\sqrt{\dfrac{x^4y^2}{225}}$ _____

Solve each inequality and graph its solution set.

11. $x + 3 < 4$ _____

12. $-3x < 12$ _____

13. $2x - 6 \geq 0$ _____

14. $5 - 3(2x - 5) \geq 8$ _____

15. $-1 < 2 + 3x < 17$ _____

16. $x > 8$ and $x < 10$ _____

17. $12 < -3 - 3x$ or $12 < -3 + 3x$ _____

18. $|x + 8| \leq 4$ _____

Solve each equation.

19. $2x^2 - 8 = 42$ _____

20. $\sqrt{12x} = 4\sqrt{3}$ _____

21. $\sqrt{2x - 4} = 6$ _____

22. $x^2 - 6x - 2 = 0$ _____

(continued)

ALGEBRA, Structure and Method, Book 1
Copyright © 1986 by Houghton Mifflin Company. All rights reserved. Printed in U.S.A.

NAME _____ DATE _____ SCORE _____

Cumulative Review—Chapters 10–12 *(continued)*

Graph.

23. $y = 2x - 3$

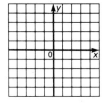

24. $x + 2y = 4$

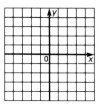

25. $y \leq 3x - 2$

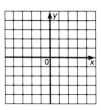

26. $y = x^2 + 2x - 3$

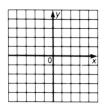

In each problem, find x.

27. _____

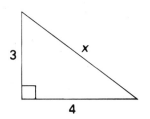

28. _____

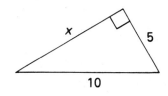

Express each number as a terminating or a repeating decimal.

29. $\dfrac{7}{20}$ _____

30. $\dfrac{7}{30}$ _____

Express each number as a fraction in simplest form.

31. 0.625 _____

32. $0.\overline{63}$ _____

Solve.

33. The sum of three consecutive odd integers is less than 200. Find the three integers with the greatest sum.

34. Find the perimeter of a rectangle whose area is 128 m² and whose length is twice its width.

35. The square of a negative number exceeds the number by 56. What is the number? _____

36. Jean's scores on three exams were 81, 56, and 70. What is the lowest score she can get on her next exam and have an average greater than 70?

Cumulative Review—Chapters 7–12

Simplify. Give answers in terms of positive exponents.

1. $\dfrac{3^2}{3^{-1}}$ _____   **2.** $(4x^{-2})^3$ _____

Simplify.

3. $7\sqrt{48}$ _____   **4.** $\sqrt{441}$ _____

5. $\sqrt{245x^4}$ _____   **6.** $\sqrt{\dfrac{1}{8}}$ _____

7. $(\sqrt{3} + 3)^2$ _____   **8.** $\dfrac{2}{\sqrt{3} - 1}$ _____

Solve.

9. $y + 8 = y^2$ _____   **10.** $\dfrac{y - 1}{y} = \dfrac{y}{4}$ _____

11. $0.92x = 32.2$ _____   **12.** $\dfrac{3 - 2y}{4} \geq \dfrac{5y + 6}{7}$ _____

13. $\dfrac{2}{5}(10x - 15) - \dfrac{1}{10}(30x - 20) = 3$ _____   **14.** $3\sqrt{2x} = 6$ _____

15. $b - \dfrac{b}{2} = 5 + \dfrac{b}{4}$ _____   **16.** $\dfrac{1}{x - 1} + \dfrac{1}{2} = \dfrac{2}{x^2 - 1}$ _____

17. $x^2 + 4x + 4 = 0$ _____   **18.** $|x + 7| < 2$ _____

Solve each system.

19. $-x + 2y = 5$
      $4x + 3y = -20$ _____   **20.** $4x + 5y = 3$
                                          $-2x + 5y = -9$ _____

21. $3x + 4y = -10$
      $x + 6 = 0$ _____   **22.** $x - y = 9$
                               $x + y = 12$ _____

(continued)

Cumulative Review—Chapters 7–12 *(continued)*

23. Find the slope of the line whose equation is $2x - y = 6$. _____

24. Find an equation in standard form for the line with x-intercept 2 and y-intercept 3. _____

25. Find an equation in standard form for the line through $(1, 2)$ and $(3, 4)$. _____

26. What percent of 800 is 96? _____

27. What number is $\dfrac{1}{2}$% of 50? _____

Write the ratio in simplest form.

28. 15 min to 3 h _____

29. 5 m to 2 km _____

30. Solve for b: $\dfrac{a}{b} = \dfrac{c}{d}$ _____

31. Express $\dfrac{5}{6}$ as a terminating or a repeating decimal. _____

32. Express $0.\overline{24}$ as a fraction in simplest form. _____

33. Write 0.0000205 in scientific notation. _____

Graph.

34. $x - 2y = 6$ 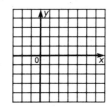   **35.** $x + 2y = 6$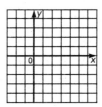

(continued)

Cumulative Review—Chapters 7–12 *(continued)*

Graph.

36. $y < -2x + 4$

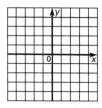

37. $x + 3 \geq 3y$

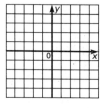

38. $f(x) = x^2 - 6x + 8$

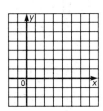

39. $y = -x^2 + 2$

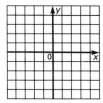

Solve.

40. A rectangle is twice as long as it is wide. Its area is 288 m². Find the dimensions of the rectangle.

_____

41. Geri paid $11.20 for a pair of gloves that were on sale for 30% off. What was the original price of the gloves?

_____

42. Find three consecutive integers such that the square of the first plus the square of the third is 102 more than the square of the second integer.

_____

43. A two-digit number is four times the sum of its digits. The number with its digits reversed is 36 more than the original number. Find the original number.

_____

ALGEBRA, Structure and Method, Book 1

Mixed Review—Chapters 1–3

Evaluate if $a = 5$, $b = -3$, and $c = 4$.

1. $\dfrac{(2a + b)}{(c - b)}$ _____

2. $3 + (-b) + c$ _____

3. $(ab) + c$ _____

4. $\dfrac{10c}{a} - b$ _____

5. $a - |b|$ _____

6. $-|a - b|$ _____

7. Margaret is four times as old as Phil. The sum of their ages is 30. Let p represent Phil's age and write an equation that represents the given information. _____

8. Graph the numbers -5, -3, 1.5, 2 on this number line.   ⊢+──+──+──+──+──+──+──+──+──+──+──+⊣

Solve. If the equation is an identity or has no root, state that fact.

9. $n + 3 = -16$ _____

10. $8 = -x + 15$ _____

11. $8y = 120$ _____

12. $15 = -\dfrac{1}{3}y$ _____

13. $5q - 2q = 48$ _____

14. $3(t + 2) - 5 = 3$ _____

15. $4(2 - x) = 2(1 - 2x)$ _____

16. $\dfrac{12}{2} + 3y = 3(y + 2)$ _____

17. Translate into symbols: The absolute value of negative five is greater than the opposite of negative three. _____

18. The sum of two numbers is 83. One number is t. What is the other number? _____

19. The sum of three consecutive even integers is 18 more than twice the largest. Find the numbers. _____

20. The formula $C = \dfrac{5}{9}(F - 32)$ states the rule for finding the Celsius temperature for any given Fahrenheit temperature. Find C if $F = -40$. _____

Simplify.

21. $3(a + 2b) + 5(2a + 3b)$ _____

22. $-5 + (-3) + (-4)$ _____

23. $\left|\dfrac{3}{4}\right| - \left|-\dfrac{3}{4}\right|$ _____

24. $\dfrac{1}{5}(34) + \dfrac{1}{5}(6)$ _____

25. $(-2)(-11)(30)$ _____

26. $-1.42 - 2.35$ _____

27. $151 - (82 - 50)$ _____

28. $-5 + 7 + (-4) + 3$ _____

29. $15(12 - 8) - 60 \div (9 + 6)$ _____

30. $5t(0.02) + 5t(1.98)$ _____

(continued)

Mixed Review—Chapters 1–3 (continued)

31. Eleven times a number is -352. What is the number? _____

32. Write in order from least to greatest:

$-2\frac{2}{3},\ -2\frac{3}{4},\ -2\frac{1}{8},\ -2\frac{15}{16}$ _____

33. If a number is decreased by 12, the result is 55. What is the number? _____

Write $<$ or $>$ in the space provided to make a true statement.

34. 0 _____ $-\dfrac{15}{4}$

35. -8 _____ 6

36. The sum of three consecutive odd integers is 71. Write an equation to represent the relationship. _____

37. The width of a rectangle is 24 cm less than the length. The perimeter is 148 cm. Find the dimensions. _____

List the letters for the points whose coordinates are given.

38. -4 _____

39. 4 _____

40. $-1\frac{1}{2}$ _____

41. Find three consecutive even integers whose sum is 48. _____

42. The Shakespeare Guild sold regular admission tickets to a play for $6 and patron's tickets for $16. The Guild sold 325 tickets for a total of $2750. How many patron's tickets did they sell? _____

ALGEBRA, Structure and Method, Book 1

Mixed Review—Chapters 1–6

Evaluate if $x = -4$, $y = -3$, and $z = 2$.

1. $\dfrac{x + 3y}{x^2 + y - 6y^2}$ _____

2. $\dfrac{x}{z} - y$ _____

3. $-|x - z|$ _____

4. $(-y^4)(-z^2)$ _____

5. $xy - z$ _____

6. $x^2 + z^3$ _____

7. Solve the equation $x^2 - x = 2$ if $x \in \{-4, -2, 0, 2, 4\}$. _____

8. Rewrite in exponential form: the fourth power of one third of y _____

9. A building has a rectangular room and a square room with equal floor space. The rectangular room is 3 m longer and 2 m narrower than the square room. Find the floor space of each. _____

Solve.

10. $(x + 4)(x - 3) = (x + 1)(x - 2)$ _____

11. $7 - y = -2$ _____

12. $5(2t - 1) + 3(3t + 4) = 4(4t + 7)$ _____

13. $m + 11 = \dfrac{1}{2}m - 3$ _____

14. $3b - 4 = 5$ _____

15. $\frac{1}{3}y = 4\frac{1}{3}$ _____

16. $3y - (5y + 4) = 12$ _____

17. $2x - 5 = -9$ _____

18. Find the average of -23, 42, 18, and 59. _____

Factor completely.

19. $6t^2 - t - 5$ _____

20. $y^2 - 6y - 55$ _____

21. $16z^2 - 9$ _____

22. $12y^3 - 3y$ _____

23. $x^4 + 22x^2 + 121$ _____

24. $185x^2y^5 + 74xy^3 - 37xy^2$ _____

Solve.

25. $y^2 - 5y + 6 = 0$ _____

26. $4n^2 - 9 = 0$ _____

27. $6x^2 - 22x = 40$ _____

28. $x^3 - 14x = 49x$ _____

(continued)

Mixed Review—Chapters 1–6 (continued)

Simplify. Assume that no denominator is zero.

29. $(x - 5)(2x - 4)$ _____

30. $(3y + 2)(3y - 2)$ _____

31. $(-3x^4)^3$ _____

32. $\dfrac{12a^5b^6}{(2a^2b)^2}$ _____

33. $(5x^2 + 3x) + (-9x - 2)$ _____

34. $(5x^2)(4xy^3)$ _____

35. $-\frac{1}{2} + 5 - 3\frac{1}{2} + 4$ _____

36. $\dfrac{t + 2}{t} + \dfrac{3}{t + 1}$ _____

37. $\dfrac{35r^3s^2t - 20rs^3 + 40r^3s^3t^2}{5rs}$ _____

38. $-4z(8 - 3z)$ _____

39. $\dfrac{3y^2}{10x^2} \cdot \dfrac{5x}{2y}$ _____

40. $(5n - 4)(3n^2 - 2n + 1)$ _____

41. $\dfrac{x - 1}{3} + \dfrac{2x - 1}{4} - \dfrac{1}{2}$ _____

42. $t^3 \cdot t^y$ _____

43. $(8a^2 - 5ab) - (3a^2b^2 - 2ab)$ _____

44. $-27 \div 3 + 6$ _____

45. $\dfrac{a^2 - b^2}{2a + b} \div \dfrac{a + b}{a - b}$ _____

46. $\dfrac{6y^2 - 3y}{4y^2 - 4y + 1}$ _____

47. $(3x^2y)^2(-5x^2y^3)^2$ _____

48. $17 - (42 - 51)$ _____

49. $\dfrac{2}{3}(16) + \dfrac{2}{3}(14)$ _____

50. $3x - 2y + 5x + 7y$ _____

51. Give the prime factorization of 396. _____

Divide. Write your answer as a polynomial or a mixed expression.

52. $\dfrac{m^2 - 3m + 5}{m - 1}$ _____

53. $\dfrac{y^3 - 1}{y - 1}$ _____

54. A vending machine contains 204 dimes, nickels, and quarters. There are 30 more dimes than nickels and 15 more quarters than dimes. How many of each type of coin are there? _____

55. A plane makes the trip from Acton to Banville at 800 km/h. The return, at 1000 km/h, takes $\dfrac{1}{2}$ h less than the initial flight. Find the distance between the towns. _____

(continued)

ALGEBRA, Structure and Method, Book 1
Copyright © 1986 by Houghton Mifflin Company. All rights reserved. Printed in U.S.A.

Mixed Review—Chapters 1–6 *(continued)*

56. Write $3 - \dfrac{5}{z+1}$ as a fraction in simplest form. _____

57. Find the missing factor: $48x^4y^7 = (2xy)^3 ($_____$)$

58. Find the LCD of $\dfrac{3}{5}$, $\dfrac{2}{3}$, and $\dfrac{5}{6}$. _____

Represent each word phrase by a variable expression.

59. Seven less than the number x. _____

60. Five more than twice the number y. _____

61. The sum of three consecutive integers is 13 less than 4 times the largest. Write an equation to describe the relationship. _____

62. Pure nitric acid has a melting point of $-41.59°C$ and a boiling point of $86°C$. Find the difference between the two temperatures. _____

63. Fifteen times a number is -360. What is the number? _____

64. Find three consecutive integers whose sum is 84. _____

65. List all pairs of negative integral factors of 48. _____

66. The sum of two numbers is 13 and the sum of their squares is 89. Find the numbers. _____

67. Find the GCF of 324 and 416. _____

ALGEBRA, Structure and Method, Book 1
Copyright © 1986 by Houghton Mifflin Company. All rights reserved. Printed in U.S.A.

Mixed Review—Chapters 1–9

Simplify.

1. $2(x - 3y) + 4(3x - y)$ _____

2. $4(6) - (8 + 1)$ _____

3. $\dfrac{2}{5} \div \dfrac{2}{3} \cdot \dfrac{5}{4}$ _____

4. $-3\frac{1}{2} + 6\frac{1}{5} - 2\frac{1}{2}$ _____

5. $\dfrac{y - 5}{y} - \dfrac{y}{y + 1}$ _____

6. $\dfrac{x^2 - xy}{5y} + \dfrac{x - y}{y^2}$ _____

7. $(2r^3s^2)^3(-rs^3)^2$ _____

8. $(2t - 3)(2t + 3)$ _____

9. The sum of three consecutive even integers is 138. Write an equation to describe the relationship. _____

10. If 27 is added to a two-digit number, the digits are reversed. The sum of the digits is 11. Find the original number. _____

11. A restaurant can prepare 20 patties from 11 kg of ground beef. How much ground beef is needed for 500 patties? _____

12. Find the slope of the line through $(5, 6)$ and $(2, -3)$. _____

13. Jack is 8 years older than Anna. Seven years ago, he was twice as old as Anna. How old is each now? _____

14. Two numbers are in the ratio $3:8$. One half of their sum is $16\frac{1}{2}$. Find the numbers. _____

15. Graph: $2x + y = 5$

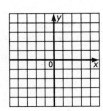

16. Solve this system graphically.

$2x - y = 1$
$x + 2y = 3$

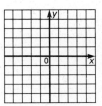

17. If y varies directly as the square of x, and $y = 18$ when $x = 3$, find y when $x = 5$. _____

18. Write an equation in standard form of:

  a. the line with slope -4 that passes through $(-5, -3)$ _____

  b. the line through $(-2, -3)$ and $(8, 5)$ _____

(continued)

ALGEBRA, Structure and Method, Book 1

Mixed Review—Chapters 1–9 *(continued)*

Solve each equation or system. If the equation or system has no solution, write "no solution."

19. $\dfrac{y-1}{2} - \dfrac{y+1}{3} = 1$ _____

20. $\dfrac{1}{x-2} + \dfrac{2}{x-1} = \dfrac{3}{x}$ _____

21. $\dfrac{3}{t+2} = \dfrac{t}{3t-2}$ _____

22. $\dfrac{12}{z-3} = \dfrac{15}{z+1}$ _____

23. $0.02x - 0.4(5-x) = 0.1$ _____

24. $5n - 6 = 3n + 8$ _____

25. $y + 5 = 11$ _____

26. $\dfrac{3x-2}{8} = \dfrac{2x-1}{8}$ _____

27. $x^2 + 5x = 14$ _____

28. $4x^2 - 12x + 9 = 0$ _____

29. $5x - 2y = 6$
    $3x - 5y = 15$ _____

30. $3x - 2y = 11$
    $5x + 2y = 13$ _____

Factor completely.

31. $x^2 - 121$ _____

32. $x^2 - 2x - 8$ _____

33. $6n^2 - 5n - 4$ _____

34. $12y^2 - 5y - 2$ _____

35. $y^2 + 23y + 132$ _____

36. $9z^4 - 25$ _____

37. The sum of the squares of two consecutive positive integers is 113. Find the numbers. _____

38. One number is 8 more than half another. The sum of the numbers is 38. Find the numbers. _____

39. Express 0.00038 in (a) scientific notation and (b) expanded notation.

    a. _____   b. _____

40. What percent of 30 is 24? _____

41. 16 is 75% of what number? _____

42. What number is $33\frac{1}{3}\%$ of 186? _____

(continued)

Mixed Review—Chapters 1–9 *(continued)*

43. A radio cost $44.10 including a 5% sales tax. What was the price without the tax? _____

44. Find the GCF of 425 and 680. _____

45. Doug can deliver his papers in 45 minutes. If Meg helps, they can finish in 20 minutes. How long would it take Meg working alone? _____

46. A dentist can schedule 15 patients in a day if she allows 24 minutes per patient. How many can she schedule if she allows 30 minutes per patient and works the same number of hours? _____

47. Three numbers are in the ratio $3:4:5$ and their sum is 228. Find the numbers. _____

48. A booster club sold cheese pizzas at $4.20 and vegetarian pizzas at $6.50 for a fund raiser. The club members sold 92 pizzas for a total of $483. How many of each type did they sell? _____

49. The sum of two numbers is 52. One number is k. What is the other number? _____

50. Find three consecutive odd integers whose sum is 3. _____

51. Translate into symbols: The sum of five and the opposite of two is greater than the absolute value of negative two. _____

52. A rectangle is twice as long as it is wide. If the length and width are both increased by 3 cm, the area is increased by 72 cm². Find the original dimensions. _____

53. If y is directly proportional to x, and $y = 40$ when $x = 12$, find y when $x = 15$. _____

54. Given that $f: x \rightarrow 3x - 2$, find:

    a. $f(0)$ _____   **b.** $f(-4)$ _____

55. Write $5 + \dfrac{4}{x - 3}$ as a fraction in simplest form. _____

56. Find the value of x if $(5, 24)$ and $(x, 16)$ are ordered pairs of the same inverse variation. _____

(continued)

ALGEBRA, Structure and Method, Book 1

Mixed Review—Chapters 1–9 (continued)

Name each set of numbers if possible. If no numbers satisfy the condition, write "no solution."

57. Three consecutive multiples of 4 whose sum is 52. _____

58. Three consecutive multiples of 3 whose sum is 252. _____

59. Jane Bentley drove 120 km on 8 L of gasoline. How far can she travel on 36 L of gasoline?   _____

60. Two trains leave a station at 2 P.M. traveling in opposite directions. One train is traveling at 100 km/h, the other at 90 km/h. At what time will they be 475 km apart?   _____

61. A grocer plans to mix two types of cereal: one that costs $3.00 per kilogram and another that costs $6.00 per kilogram. How many kilograms of each type of cereal should be mixed in order to have 15 kilograms of a cereal worth $4.80 per kilogram?   _____

62. Express $(-3y^{-3})^3$ in terms of positive exponents. _____

63. Find the least value of the function f if $f: x \rightarrow 2x^2 - 4x + 8$. _____

64. Solve $\dfrac{3}{x-1} = \dfrac{5}{2y+1}$ for y in terms of x. _____

ALGEBRA, Structure and Method, Book 1

Mixed Review—Chapters 1–12

Simplify. Assume that no denominator equals zero. Each variable represents a positive real number.

1. $(3t - 2)(2t^2 + 5t + 4)$ _____

2. $\sqrt{x^2 + 10x + 25}$ _____

3. $(4x^2y)^3(-x^5y)^2$ _____

4. $\sqrt{2601}$ _____

5. $\dfrac{b - 3}{b + 1} - \dfrac{8}{b}$ _____

6. $\sqrt{\dfrac{48}{147}}$ _____

7. $\sqrt{180}$ _____

8. $\sqrt{144s^2t^5}$ _____

9. $\sqrt{175}$ _____

10. $\sqrt{\dfrac{36x^7}{25x}}$ _____

11. Alice is three times as old as Archie. If Archie's present age is x, represent each person's age 7 years from now. _____

12. The width of a rectangle is 24 cm less than the length. The perimeter is less than 172 cm. Find the maximum dimensions of the rectangle if each dimension, in centimeters, is an integer. _____

Factor completely, if possible. If the expression is not factorable, write "prime."

13. $3x^2 + x - 2$ _____

14. $y^2 - 5y - 40$ _____

15. $4n^2 + 24n + 9$ _____

16. $x^2 - 18x + 36$ _____

17. $-48y^2 + 29y + 15$ _____

18. $3c^2 - 5cd - 12d^2$ _____

19. If r varies jointly as s and t, and $r = 90$ when $s = 8$ and $t = 15$, find r when $s = 7$ and $t = 12$. _____

20. At noon, two trains leave stations at opposite ends of the line on parallel tracks. One train is traveling at 90 km/h and the other at 96 km/h. If the stations are 651 km apart, how long will it be before the trains meet? _____

21. Express $\dfrac{x - 1}{3}$, $\dfrac{x}{4}$, and $\dfrac{1}{2}$ with their LCD. _____

Solve and graph the solution set.

22. $-2x < 6$ _____

23. $-3 \le x + 1 \le 1$ _____

24. $3z - 2 > 7$ or $2z + 1 < 5$ _____

25. $|t - 5| < 1$ _____

(continued)

ALGEBRA, Structure and Method, Book 1
Copyright © 1986 by Houghton Mifflin Company. All rights reserved. Printed in U.S.A.

Mixed Review—Chapters 1–12 (continued)

26. Approximate $\sqrt{46}$ to the nearest tenth. _____

27. The hypotenuse of a right triangle and one leg have lengths of 12 and 7 respectively. Find the length of the other leg to the nearest tenth. _____

28. The numerator of a fraction is 10 less than the denominator. If 4 is added to each, the value of the resulting fraction is $\dfrac{3}{5}$. Find the original fraction. _____

Solve each equation or inequality.

29. $\dfrac{4}{x + 6} = \dfrac{8}{3x + 5}$ _____

30. $\sqrt{\dfrac{3x - 1}{2}} = 4$ _____

31. $\sqrt{y} = \dfrac{2}{3}$ _____

32. $\dfrac{1}{3} < 2 - \dfrac{3}{4}y$ _____

33. $5t^2 - 80 = 0$ _____

34. $3t + 2 = 2t - 1$ _____

35. $3t + 2 < 5t - 3$ _____

36. $(x + 3)^2 = 16$ _____

Solve each system.

37. $x + y = 7$
$\quad\;\; 2x + 3y = 4$ _____

38. $5x - 4y = 9$
$\quad\;\; 3x + 2y = 1$ _____

39. Divide $3y^2 - 2y + 1$ by $y + 4$. _____

40. The sum of two consecutive even integers is less than 84. Find the pair with the greatest sum. _____

Use the discriminant to determine how many real-number roots the equation has. Do not solve the equation.

41. $x^2 - 3x + 5 = 0$ _____

42. $4k^2 - 12k + 9 = 0$ _____

43. When 3 times a number is increased by 7, the square root of the result is 7. Find the number. _____

Express each rational number as a terminating or repeating decimal.

44. $\dfrac{18}{25}$ _____

45. $\dfrac{13}{15}$ _____

46. $1\frac{4}{9}$ _____

47. Graph: $2x + y < 3$

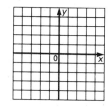

48. Graph the solution set of this system.

$x + y \geq 2$
$x - y \geq 1$

(continued)

Mixed Review—Chapters 1-12 (continued)

Express in simplest form.

49. $(5\sqrt{7} - 2\sqrt{5})(4\sqrt{7} + 3\sqrt{5})$ _____

50. $3\sqrt{3}(4\sqrt{27} - 5\sqrt{12})$ _____

51. $(2\sqrt{5} - 5\sqrt{2})^2$ _____

52. $\sqrt{\dfrac{2}{3}} \cdot \sqrt{\dfrac{8}{12}}$ _____

53. $6\sqrt{48} - 5\sqrt{18}$ _____

54. $\sqrt{3}\sqrt{15}$ _____

55. Write an equation in standard form for the line with slope -1 that passes through

$(-6, 4)$. _____

Solve using the quadratic formula. Leave irrational answers in simplest radical form.

56. $3t^2 + 5t + 2 = 0$ _____

57. $2z^2 - 7z + 4 = 0$ _____

58. Express $4.\overline{3}$ as a fraction in simplest form. _____

59. Find the slope of the line through $(-3, 5)$ and $(-4, 7)$. _____

60. Find the greatest common monomial factor: $18a^3b^4c^2$, $54a^2bc^5$, $27a^7x^2c^3$ _____

61. Evaluate: $\dfrac{3^{-2} \cdot 3^5}{3^{-3}}$ _____

62. The sum of two numbers is 12 and the sum of their squares is 78. Find the numbers. _____

ALGEBRA, Structure and Method, Book 1
Copyright © 1986 by Houghton Mifflin Company. All rights reserved. Printed in U.S.A.

Puzzles (For use with Chapter 1 of text)

1. Three boxes are in a room. You know that one contains apples, one contains oranges, and one contains a mixture of apples and oranges, but you don't know the contents of the specific boxes. The boxes are labeled "apples," "oranges," and "apples and oranges," but each box has the wrong label on it. You must identify the contents of each box by picking only one piece of fruit from only one box. You are not allowed to feel the fruit! How can you identify the contents of each box?

_____

_____

_____

2. Susan Teacher, John Writer, and Mary Potter work as a teacher, a writer, and a potter. No one, however, works at the occupation that corresponds to his or her last name. Each person has a child with the same last name that assists one of the other two. No child works at the occupation that corresponds to his or her last name. If John Writer is not a potter, what does Susan Teacher's child do?

_____

3. You probably know someone who will be x years old in the year x^2. When was that person born? _____

4. In a set of eight coins, seven weigh the same amount and one is lighter than the others. How can you find the lighter coin in only two weighings using a pair of balance scales?

_____

_____

_____

5. Suppose the following statements are true.
It takes a minimum of four United States coins to buy an apple.
To buy two apples, you need a minimum of six coins.
To buy three apples you need no more than two coins.
How much does the apple cost?

_____

6. This 6×8 rectangle has just as many square tiles along its border as there are square tiles in the interior—namely, 24. Can you find any other rectangle that has as many square tiles along its border as there are in its interior? If so, name it.

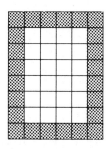

_____

Number Arrays (For use with Chapter 2 of text)

In this array of nonnegative integers, notice that the left-hand column consists of the multiples of 5. The multiples of 5 can be thought of as numbers of the form $5n$ where $n \in \{0, 1, 2, 3, \ldots\}$. The numbers in the next column are of the form $5n + 1$; the numbers in the next column are of the form $5n + 2$; the numbers in the next column are of the form $5n + 3$; and the numbers in the last column are of the form $5n + 4$. In what column will the number 54,321 appear? Since 54,321 can be written in the form

$$54{,}321 = 5(10{,}864) + 1$$

we can conclude that 54,321 will appear in the second column; that is, the one headed by 1.

0	1	2	3	4
5	6	7	8	9
10	11	12	13	14
15	16	17	18	19
20	21	22	23	24
:	:	:	:	:

In Exercises 1–4, study each listing and determine the answer to this question: In which column will the number 10,000 appear?

1.

0	1	2	3	4	5	6	7
8	9	10	11	12	13	14	15
16	17	18	19	20	21	22	23
24	25	26	27	28	29	30	31
:	:	:	:	:	:	:	:

_____

2.

0	2	4	6	8	10
12	14	16	18	20	22
24	26	28	30	32	34
36	38	40	42	44	46
:	:	:	:	:	:

_____

(continued)

ALGEBRA, Structure and Method, Book 1

Number Arrays (continued)

3.

0	1	4	9	16	25
36	49	64	81	100	121
144	169	·	·	·	·
:	:	:	:	:	:

_____

4.

1	2	3	4	5	6	7	8
9	10	11	12	13	14	15	16
17	18	19	20	21	22	23	24
:	:	:	:	:	:	:	:

_____

5. Suppose someone picks a number in the array below and tells you the sum of the four diagonally opposite numbers around the selected number. For example, if the person selects the number 17, the four diagonally opposite numbers are 9, 25, 23, and 11; the sum of these four numbers is 68. Do you see any relationship between the sum and the selected number? If so, describe it.

_____

1	2	3	4	5	6	7
8	9	10	11	12	13	14
15	16	17	18	19	20	21
22	23	24	25	26	27	28
:	:	:	:	:	:	:

Study the array. If x is the selected number and you are told that the sum of the four diagonally opposite numbers is 212, how can you determine what number x is?

_____

Suppose y is the selected number and s is the sum of the four diagonally opposite numbers. Write an equation that shows the relationship between y and s.

_____

(continued)

Number Arrays *(continued)*

6. In the array below, select one number from the column headed by 4 and another from the column headed by 5. The sum of the two numbers will appear in the column headed by 2. Use algebraic expressions to show why this is so.

0	1	2	3	4	5	6
7	8	9	10	11	12	13
14	15	16	17	18	19	20
21	22	23	24	25	26	27
⋮	⋮	⋮	⋮	⋮	⋮	⋮

_____

_____

_____

_____

ALGEBRA, Structure and Method, Book 1

Squares in a Rectangle (For use with Chapter 3 of text)

1. The figure below shows a rectangle that has been divided into nine squares, all of different dimensions. The smallest square has sides 1 unit long, and the sides of two of the other squares have been labeled. Write an equation that will yield the value of x. (*Hint:* First complete the labeling of the sides of the squares. Then, to write the equation to find x, use the fact that opposite sides of a rectangle are equal.)

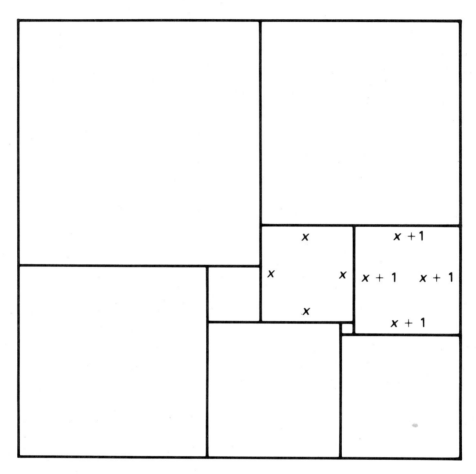

Equation _____

Solution _____

(continued)

Squares in a Rectangle *(continued)*

2. This rectangle has been divided into eleven squares. Write an equation that will yield the value of *x*.

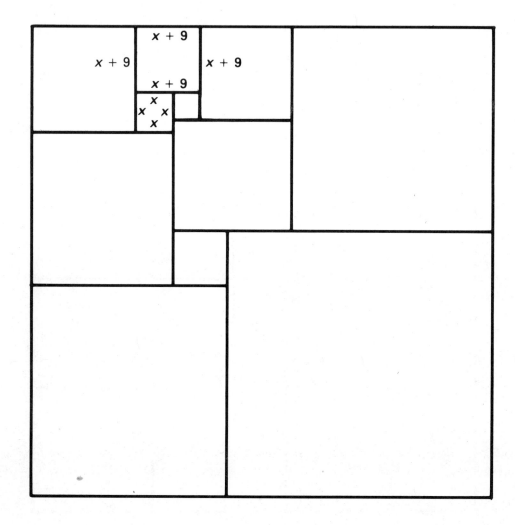

Equation _____

Solution _____

ALGEBRA, Structure and Method, Book 1

Exponents and Polynomials (For use with Chapter 4 of text)

1. Here are 3^6 dots arranged in a square. How many dots are there on each side of the square? Try to find the answer without actually counting the dots.

   _____

2. Suppose a square array of dots contains M^{2N} dots. How many dots are there along each side of the square? _____

In Exercises 3–5, multiply to find each product. Then look for a pattern that you can use to answer the question in Exercise 6.

3. $(x - 1)(x^2 + x + 1)$ _____

4. $(x - 1)(x^3 + x^2 + x + 1)$ _____

5. $(x - 1)(x^4 + x^3 + x^2 + x + 1)$ _____

6. What do you think the product of $x - 1$ and $x^{100} + x^{99} + x^{98} + \cdots + x + 1$ will be? _____

In Exercises 7–10, multiply to find each product. Then look for a pattern that you can use to answer the question in Exercise 11.

7. $(x + 1)(x^2 - x + 1)$ _____

8. $(x + 1)(x^3 - x^2 + x - 1)$ _____

9. $(x + 1)(x^4 - x^3 + x^2 - x + 1)$ _____

10. $(x + 1)(x^5 - x^4 + x^3 - x^2 + x - 1)$ _____

11. What do you think the product of $x + 1$ and $x^{100} - x^{99} + x^{98} - \cdots - x + 1$ will be? _____

Factoring (For use with Chapter 5 of text)

Instead of using a calculator to evaluate a numerical expression, it is sometimes easier to rewrite the expression as a simpler one and then evaluate. For example, consider $(876,889)^2 - (123,111)^2$. This expression can be rewritten as

$$(876,889 + 123,111)(876,889 - 123,111) = (1,000,000)(753,778)$$

and the product can be named easily: 753,778,000,000.

Rewrite as a simpler expression.

1. $(1,234,567,890)^2 + (1,234,567,890)(8,765,432,110)$ _____

2. $(1,000,000,011)(999,999,989)$ _____

3. $2(1,234,567,890) - (1,234,567,889)(1,234,567,891)$ _____

4. $(987,654)^2 - (12,346)^2$ _____

5. Find the value of $x^2 - 2xy + y^2$ when $x = 987,654,321$ and $y = 987,654,320$. _____

In Exercises 6–7, you are asked to look at some patterns, generalize, and then show that your generalization is correct.

6. Multiply $(3)(5)$; $(7)(9)$; $(11)(13)$. Use your answers to predict the answer to $(999)(1001)$. Using algebraic expressions, generalize to show that the product of any two consecutive odd numbers is always 1 less than a perfect square.

_____

_____

_____

7. Tell whether each of these sums is divisible by 4: $1 + 2 + 3 + 4$; $28 + 29 + 30 + 31$; $95 + 96 + 97 + 98$. Use your answers to predict whether $999 + 1000 + 1001 + 1002$ is divisible by 4. Using algebraic expressions, generalize to show whether the sum of any four consecutive integers is divisible by 4.

_____

_____

_____

8. Show that $[BC]^2 + [B^2 + C^2][B + C]^2$ is a perfect square.

_____

_____

_____

ALGEBRA, Structure and Method, Book 1

Fractions and Computers (For use with Chapter 6 of text)

How would a computer evaluate the number 6/5/4? It would read from left to right and interpret the expression as (6/5)/4. The computer would evaluate the number as 0.3 since $\dfrac{6}{5} \div 4 = \dfrac{6}{5} \times \dfrac{1}{4} = \dfrac{3}{10} = 0.3$. In general, $(A/B)/C$ would be evaluated as $\dfrac{A}{B} \div C = \dfrac{A}{B} \times \dfrac{1}{C} = \dfrac{A}{BC}$. Next consider the expression $A/(B/C)$. The computer would evaluate $A/(B/C)$ as $A \div \dfrac{B}{C} = A \times \dfrac{C}{B} = \dfrac{AC}{B}$. It is clear that $(A/B)/C$ is not generally equal to $A/(B/C)$.

Suppose we were to divide four numbers. The computer would evaluate $A/B/C/D$ by reading from left to right. It would first divide A by B; then it would divide that answer by C; finally it would divide that answer by D. Verify that the expression 6/5/4/3 would be evaluated as 0.1.

Evaluate the following.

1. (8/6)/(4/2) _____

2. 8/(6/(4/2)) _____

3. (8/(6/4))/2 _____

4. 8/((6/4)/2) _____

5. ((8/6)/4)/2 _____

6. Which two of the expressions in Exercises 1–5 are equal in value? Do you think this is a coincidence? Using A, B, C, and D (in place of 8, 4, 6, and 2), show whether the two expressions will always be equal in value.

_____

_____

_____

Evaluate the following.

7. $(A/B)/(C/D)$ _____

8. $((A/B)/C)/D$ _____

9. $A/(B/(C/D))$ _____

10. $(A/(B/C))/D$ _____

11. $A/((B/C)/D)$ _____

12. Which of the fractions in Exercises 7–11 are equal? _____

13. Which fraction is equal to $\dfrac{A}{BCD}$? _____

14. Which fractions are equal to $\dfrac{AC}{BD}$? _____

15. What would a computer print for 225/2/2/5? _____

16. What would a computer print for 6/5/4/3/2? _____

Experimenting with Fractions (For use with Chapter 7 of text)

The expression at the right may look strange to you. It can, however, be evaluated easily. Since $\frac{1}{1} = 1$, the expression equals $\frac{1}{1 + 1}$, or $\frac{1}{2}$.

$$\cfrac{1}{1 + \cfrac{1}{1}}$$

Evaluate each of the following. Express your answer as a fraction.

1. $\quad 1 + \cfrac{1}{1 + \cfrac{1}{1}}$

2. $\quad \cfrac{1}{1 + \cfrac{1}{1 + \cfrac{1}{1}}}$

3. If the expression in Exercise 1 is represented as a, how would you represent the expression in Exercise 2? What is the relationship between the expressions in Exercises 1 and 2?

Evaluate each of the following.

4. $\quad \cfrac{1}{1 - \cfrac{1}{1 + \cfrac{1}{1 + \cfrac{1}{1}}}}$

5. $\quad \cfrac{1}{1 + \cfrac{1}{1 - \cfrac{1}{1 + \cfrac{1}{1 + 1}}}}$

Try to express each of the following numbers using expressions similar to the ones in Exercises 2, 4, and 5.

6. $\dfrac{4}{5}$

7. $\dfrac{8}{13}$

ALGEBRA, Structure and Method, Book 1

Patterns in Systems of Equations (For use with Chapter 8 of text)

Solve each system of equations.

1. $2x + y = 15$
$x + 2y = 15$ _____

2. $3x - y = 8$
$-x + 3y = 8$ _____

3. $2x + 3y = 5$
$3x + 2y = 5$ _____

4. $5x - 2y = 9$
$-2x + 5y = 9$ _____

5. Find the pattern in Exercises 1–4. Then predict the values that are the solution to the following system of equations.

$$987x + 13y = 100$$
$$13x + 987y = 100$$ _____

6. Why are the *x*- and *y*-values equal in the above examples?

_____

7. Solve this system of three equations.

$$x + 2y + 3z = 3$$
$$2x + 3y + z = 3$$
$$3x + y + 2z = 3$$ _____

One way to solve a system of equations such as

$$x + 2y = 5$$
$$2x + y = 1$$

is to add the equations as they are. You will then have $3x + 3y = 6$. Dividing both sides by 3, you obtain $x + y = 2$. It is now fairly easy to rewrite the first equation $x + 2y = 5$ as $(x + y) + y = 5$, which is the same as $2 + y = 5$. Therefore, $y = 3$. Since $x + 2y = 5$, you obtain $x + 6 = 5$; so $x = -1$.

Use the technique described above to solve each of these systems of equations.

8. $x + 3y = 7$
$3x + y = 5$ _____

9. $x + y \quad\; = 4$
$\quad\;\; y + z = -7$
$x \quad\;\; + z = 5$ _____

10. $x + y - z = 4$
$x - y + z = 1$
$-x + y + z = 5$ _____

Making Curves into Lines (For use with Chapter 9 of text)

If the following data is graphed, it would be difficult to
find an equation for the curve.

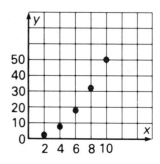

x	2	4	6	8	10
y	2	8	18	32	50

Now suppose we let $X = x^2$ and plot x^2 and y (rather than x and y). Then the graph becomes a line. We can find an
equation for the line, and then we can find an equation for the original data.

$X = x^2$	4	16	36	64	100
y	2	8	18	32	50

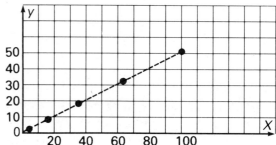

The line has a slope of $\dfrac{1}{2}$ and passes through the point (4, 2). An equation for the line is

$$y = \frac{1}{2}X$$

Since $\dfrac{1}{2}X = \dfrac{1}{2}x^2$, the equation for the original data is $y = \dfrac{1}{2}x^2$.

In each exercise, complete the second table, plot the points, and see if the new data yield a line. Find an equation
for the line. Then write an equation for the original data. (The given decimal values are not necessarily exact.)

1.

x	2	4	6	8
y	6	24	54	96

$X = x^2$				
y	6	24	54	96

_____

_____

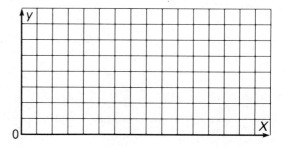

(continued)

ALGEBRA, Structure and Method, Book 1
Copyright © 1986 by Houghton Mifflin Company. All rights reserved. Printed in U.S.A.

Making Curves into Lines *(continued)*

2.

x	1	2	3	4
y	3	4.2	5.1	6

$X = \sqrt{x}$

y	3	4.2	5.1	6

_____

_____

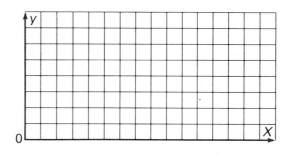

3.

x	3	4	5	6
y	6	10.7	16.7	24

$X = x^2$

y	6	10.7	16.7	24

_____

_____

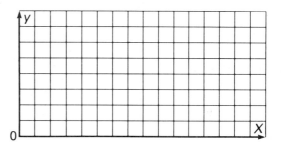

Find an equation for each set of data. (The decimal values are not necessarily exact.) If the y-values appear to be decreasing as the x-values increase, you might let $X = \dfrac{1}{x}$ and plot y against X $\left(\text{that is, } \dfrac{1}{x}\right)$.

4.

x	2	4	6	8
y	0.5	2	4.5	8

_____

_____

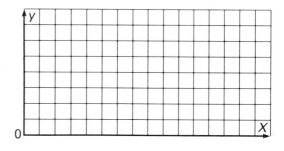

5.

x	3	5	7	9
y	1.67	1	0.71	0.56

_____

_____

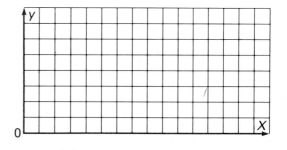

NAME _____ DATE _____ SCORE _____

Reciprocals of Integers (For use with Chapter 10 of text)

1. Find three different positive integers A, B, and C such that $\dfrac{1}{A} + \dfrac{1}{B} = \dfrac{1}{C}$. Then compare your answer with those of your classmates to see if you can recognize some patterns.

_____

2. Add these two expressions and simplify the answer.

$$\dfrac{1}{x(x + y)} + \dfrac{1}{y(x + y)}$$ _____

3. How can the given expressions and the result in Exercise 2 help you to find other values of A, B, and C that satisfy the equation $\dfrac{1}{A} + \dfrac{1}{B} = \dfrac{1}{C}$ (Exercise 1)?

_____

_____

4. Find four different positive integers A, B, C, and D such that $\dfrac{1}{A} + \dfrac{1}{B} + \dfrac{1}{C} = \dfrac{1}{D}$.

_____

ALGEBRA, Structure and Method, Book 1

Rectangles (For use with Chapter 11 of text)

Two rectangles are said to have the same shape if the ratio of their long sides is equal to the ratio of their short sides. Rectangle *QRST* has the same shape as rectangle *WXYZ*, since $\dfrac{8}{4} = \dfrac{6}{3}$.

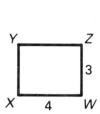

Pictured below is a rectangle with the interesting property that if it is cut in half along the dotted line, then the two halves will each have the same shape as the original sheet. Such a rectangular sheet is called a *folio* sheet.

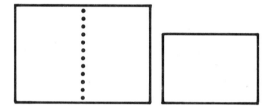

1. If the original rectangle is 20 cm wide, how long must it be? _____

2. Is a sheet of paper 17 cm by 12 cm a folio sheet? Why?

   _____

3. What is the ratio of the length to the width of a folio sheet? Can a folio sheet have integers for its length and width? _____

4. Suppose you have an $a \times b$ piece of folio paper $(a > b)$. If you cut off a square of dimensions $b \times b$, will the remaining rectangle be a folio sheet?

   _____

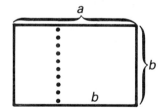

5. A standard sheet of paper used in the United States is $8\frac{1}{2} \times 11$ inches. Is this a folio sheet? _____

Geometric Pictures and Algebraic Facts (For use with Chapter 12 of text)

Each picture illustrates an algebraic fact. Complete each statement.

1.

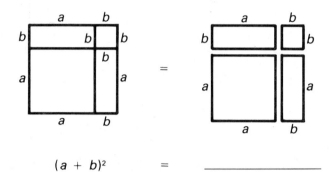

$(a + b)^2$ = _____

2.

a^2 + b^2 = $(a + b)^2$ − _____

3.

$x^2 + bx$ = $x^2 + \dfrac{b}{2}x + \dfrac{b}{2}x$ = $\left(x + \dfrac{b}{2}\right)^2$ − _____

4.

a^2 − b^2 = $\dfrac{1}{2}(a - b)(a + b)$ + _____ = _____

Using Charts in Solving Problems (For use with Section 3–6)

By working through the steps in the problems below, you will gain skill in using charts to help solve problems.

Problem 1   Uncle Louis is three times as old as Michelle. In eight years their ages will total 100. How old are they now?

a. What does the problem ask you to find?

_____

b. Suppose x represents Michelle's age now. Write an expression for Michelle's age 8 years from now.   _____

c. Michelle is x years old now. Uncle Louis is three times as old as Michelle. Write an expression for Uncle Louis's age now.   _____

d. Using the expression that you found in part **c,** write an expression for Uncle Louis's age 8 years from now.   _____

e. Complete this chart using the expressions that you found in parts **b, c,** and **d.**

	Age now	Age in 8 years
Michelle	x	
Uncle Louis		

f. "In eight years their ages will total 100" means that

$$\text{Michelle's age in 8 years} + \text{Uncle Louis's age in 8 years} = 100$$

Write an equation that states this relationship.

_____

g. Solve your equation for x. Then find $3x$.   _____

h. Write your answer to the problem.

_____

i. Check your results with the statement of the problem.

Is Uncle Louis three times as old as Michelle?   _____

In eight years will their ages total 100?   _____

(continued)

Using Charts in Solving Problems *(continued)*

Problem 2   Idaho became a state of the United States 40 years after California. In 1900, California had been a state five times as long as Idaho. How many years will California have been a state by 1990?

a. Complete: The problem asks you to find the number of years that _____ will have been a state in the year _____.

b. Let x = California statehood age in 1990. (Note that this is what you need to find.) Write an expression for California's age in 1900 (in terms of x). _____

c. Remember that Idaho became a state 40 years *after* California did. Write an expression for Idaho's statehood age in 1990 (in terms of x). _____

d. In terms of x, what was Idaho's age in 1900? _____

e. Complete this chart using your answers in parts **b, c,** and **d.**

	Age in 1990	*Age in 1900*
California	x	
Idaho		

f. The problem states that in 1900, California had been a state five times as long as Idaho. Use this statement and the chart to write an equation for the problem.

_____

g. Solve your equation. _____

h. Write your answer to the problem. _____

i. Check your results with the statement of the problem.

In 1900, California's age was _____ years and Idaho's age was _____ years. Do these values agree with the given facts of the problem? _____

How many years will California have been a state by 1990? _____

ALGEBRA, Structure and Method, Book 1

Cost and Value Problems (For use with Section 3–7)

By working through the steps in the problems below, you will gain skill in solving problems involving cost, wages, and value.

Problem 1 Marina Perez bought some containers of windshield washer fluid for 99¢ each and some ice scrapers for 69¢ each. She bought 6 items in all and spent $2.58 more on windshield washer fluid than on ice scrapers. How many of each did she buy?

a. What do you need to find? _____

_____

b. Let x = the number of ice scrapers Marina bought. How many containers of windshield washer fluid did she buy? (Reread the problem if you need help.) _____

c. Complete this chart.

	Number	× Price (in dollars) =	Cost
Ice scrapers	x	0.69	
Windshield washer fluid			

d. Notice that Marina spent $2.58 more on windshield washer fluid than on ice scrapers.

Cost of windshield washer fluid = Cost of ice scrapers + 2.58

_____ = _____ + 2.58

e. Solve to find the value of x. Then find $6 - x$. _____

f. Write your answer to the problem. _____

_____

g. Check your results with the statement of the problem.

Did Marina buy 6 items in all? _____

How much did the windshield washer fluid cost? _____

How much did the ice scrapers cost? _____

What is the difference between these costs? _____

(continued)

Cost and Value Problems (continued)

Problem 2   Chong Wun has $440 in twenty-dollar, ten-dollar, and five-dollar bills. The numbers of twenties, tens, and fives are consecutive integers in the order given. How many bills does he have in all?

a. Let n = the number of $20 bills. Then:

_____ =   the number of $10 bills,

_____ =   the number of $5 bills, and

_____ =   the total number of bills.

b. Which formula should you use in setting up a chart for this problem?

_____

c. Complete the chart.

	Number	Value	Total value
$20 bills	n		
$10 bills			
$5 bills			

d. Which fact given in the problem is *not* shown in the chart?

_____

e. Use this fact to write an equation for the problem.

_____

f. Solve to find the value of n.

_____

g. Now complete this chart with *numerals*.

	Number	Value	Total value
$20 bills			
$10 bills			
$5 bills			

h. Write your answer to the problem. _____

i. Check your results with the statement of the problem.

Are the numbers of twenty-dollar, ten-dollar, and five-dollar bills consecutive integers? _____

What is their total value? _____

ALGEBRA, Structure and Method, Book 1

Distance-Rate-Time Problems (For use with Section 4–8)

By working through the steps in the problems below, you will gain skill in solving problems involving distance, rate, and time.

Problem 1   Two cars left Daisy's Diner at the same time and traveled in opposite directions. One car traveled for 78 min. The other car traveled for 144 min at a rate 5 km/h faster than the first car. If the faster car went twice as far as the slower car, how far did each car travel?

a. Since the rate is given in km/h, express the *times* in hours, using decimals.

Slower car: Time = 78 min = _____ h

Faster car: Time = 144 min = _____ h

b. Let r = the slower car's speed in km/h. Complete the chart.

	Rate	×	Time	=	Distance
Slower car	r				
Faster car					

c. Use the information in the chart to draw a sketch for the problem. Label the sketch.

d. Which given fact is *not* used in the chart? _____

_____

e. Use the chart, the sketch, and the fact in part **d** to write an equation for the problem.

_____

f. Solve the equation, and find a numerical value for each car's speed.

Slower car _____   Faster car _____

g. Notice that finding the cars' speeds does not answer the question in the problem. What does the question ask you

to find? _____

h. Write your answer to the question in the problem.

_____

i. Check: Did the faster car travel twice as far as the slower car? _____

(continued)

Distance-Rate-Time Problems *(continued)*

Problem 2   At 10:00 A.M. a car left the service station on Route 209 heading south at 86 km/h. At 10:30 A.M. another car left the station and headed south at 80 km/h. At what time were the cars 55 km apart?

a. What does the problem ask you to find? _____

_____

b. Let t = the faster car's traveling time in hours. Write an expression for the slower car's traveling time in hours.

_____

c. Complete the chart.

	Rate	×	Time	=	Distance
Faster car			t		
Slower car					

d. Draw a sketch for the problem and label each arrow with the appropriate expression.

e. At the required time, the cars were 55 km apart. This means that the *difference* between the distances traveled equals 55 km. Write an equation for the problem.

_____

f. Solve to find the value of t. _____

g. Notice that finding the value of t does not answer the question in the problem. What does the question ask you to find?

_____

h. Find the answer to the question in the problem. _____

i. Check your results with the statement of the problem.

For the cars to be 55 km apart, the faster car must have traveled 55 km farther than the slower car by the time

you named in your answer. _____

(continued)

ALGEBRA, Structure and Method, Book 1

Distance-Rate-Time Problems *(continued)*

Problem 3   Jenny's house is 7 km from Karen's house. Each girl left her house at the same time heading toward the other's house. Jenny walked, Karen rode her bike, and the two met in just half an hour. If Karen's speed was 1 km/h less than twice Jenny's speed, how much farther did Karen travel than Jenny?

a. Let j = Jenny's walking speed in km/h. Write an expression for Karen's riding speed. _____

b. Complete the chart.

	Rate	×	Time	=	Distance
Jenny	j				
Karen					

c. Draw a sketch for the problem. Label each arrow in the sketch.

d. What was the total distance traveled? _____

e. Write an equation for the problem.

_____

f. Solve to find the value of j. _____

g. Is the value of j the answer to the question in the problem? _____

h. Find the distance Jenny walked. _____   Find the distance Karen rode. _____

i. Find the answer to the question in the problem. _____

j. Check your results with the original statement of the problem.

What is the sum of the distances traveled by Jenny and Karen? _____

Did the two girls meet in just half an hour? _____

Distance-Rate-Time Problems *(continued)*

Problem 4   A small boat traveled upstream on a river at 10 km/h and returned downstream to its starting point at 14 km/h. If the round trip took 6 h in all, how far upstream did the boat travel?

a. Since the problem involves a round trip, what must be true of the distance traveled upstream and the distance traveled downstream? _____

b. Was the time spent going upstream equal to the time spent going downstream? _____ Explain your answer. _____

_____

c. Let x = the number of hours spent traveling upstream. Write an expression for the time spent traveling downstream. _____

d. Complete the chart.

	Rate	×	Time	=	Distance
Upstream					
Downstream					

e. Draw and label a sketch for the problem.

f. Write an equation for the problem. _____

g. Solve your equation. _____

h. Notice that finding the value of x does not answer the question. What *does* the question ask you to find?

_____

i. Answer the question. _____

j. Check your results with the statement of the problem.

Find the distance in each direction.

Upstream: _____ × _____ = _____

Downstream: _____ × _____ = _____

Did the trip take 6 h in all? _____

ALGEBRA, Structure and Method, Book 1

Area Problems (For use with Section 4–9)

By working through the steps in the problems below, you will gain skill in solving area problems.

Problem 1   The width of a rectangle is two thirds of the length. If each dimension is decreased by 3 cm, the area is decreased by 66 cm². Find the original dimensions.

a. Let x = the length of the first rectangle. Write an expression for the width of the original rectangle.

_____

b. Complete the chart.

	Length	×	Width	=	Area
First rectangle	x				
Second rectangle					

c. Write an equation for the problem.

   Area of second rectangle   =   Area of first rectangle   −   66 cm²

_____   =   _____   −   _____

d. Solve your equation to find the value of x.   _____

e. Find the answer to the problem.   _____

f. Check your results with the statement of the problem.

   Is the width of the original rectangle two thirds of the length?   _____

   Find the numerical area of each rectangle. What should the difference between these areas be?   _____

   Is it?   _____

(continued)

Area Problems (continued)

Problem 2   An office building is 8 m longer than it is wide. A walkway that is 0.5 m wide surrounds the building. If the area of the walkway is 33 m², find the dimensions of the building.

a. Let x = the building's width in meters. Write an expression for the length of the building.

_____

b. Remember that the walkway is 0.5 m wide. Write an expression for the width of the outer rectangle. _____

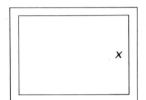

c. Write an expression for the length of the outer rectangle.

_____

d. Complete the chart.

	Length	×	Width	=	Area
Inner rectangle			x		
Outer rectangle					

e. To write an algebraic expression for the area of the walkway, you subtract, using the areas of the two rectangles.

Area of walkway: Area of outer rectangle   −   Area of inner rectangle

_____   −   _____

f. The problem states that the area of the walkway is 33 m². Write an equation for the problem.

_____

g. Solve the equation to find the value of x. _____

h. Find the answer to the problem. _____

i. Find the numerical areas of the inner rectangle, the outer rectangle, and the walkway.

Inner rectangle: _____   Outer rectangle: _____

Walkway: _____

Check that these areas agree with the facts of the problem. _____

Check also that the length of the building is 8 m greater than its width. _____

ALGEBRA, Structure and Method, Book 1
Copyright © 1986 by Houghton Mifflin Company. All rights reserved. Printed in U.S.A.

Mixture Problems (For use with Section 7–7)

By working through the steps in the problems below, you will gain skill in solving mixture problems.

Problem 1   A food processing company produces grated cheese made from parmesan and romano cheeses. Parmesan costs $3.50 per kilogram and romano costs $5.00 per kilogram. How many kilograms of each type of cheese should be used to produce 100 kg of the mixture worth $3.95 per kilogram?

a. Complete: The number of kilograms of each type of cheese used must be between _____ kg and _____ kg.

b. What formula do you need to use to solve this problem?

_____

c. Let p = the number of kilograms of parmesan cheese used. Write an expression for the number of kilograms of romano cheese used. _____

d. Complete the chart.

	Number of kilograms	×	Price per kilogram	=	Cost
Parmesan	p				
Romano					
Mixture					

e. Cost of parmesan used + cost of romano used = _____

f. Write an equation for the problem. _____

g. Solve the equation to find the value of p. _____

h. Answer the question. _____

i. Check by substituting each amount in dollars:

cost of parmesan used + cost of romano used =   cost of mixture

$ _____ + $ _____ = $ _____

Problem 2   Suppose you invest $4000 in tax-free bonds that pay $10\frac{1}{2}$% annual interest. At what annual interest rate do you need to invest $1000 in a certificate of deposit to achieve an average rate of interest of 10%?

a. Express $10\frac{1}{2}$% and 10% as decimals. _____

b. What formula do you need to solve the problem? _____

(continued)

Mixture Problems (continued)

c. Complete: Average interest rate = total interest divided by _____

d. Let r = the required annual interest rate for the certificate of deposit. Complete the chart.

	Principal	×	Rate	=	Interest
Certificate			r		
Bonds					
Total investments					

e. Complete with the correct phrases: Total interest earned =

_____ + _____

f. Write an equation for the problem. _____

g. Solve the equation. _____

h. Answer the question. (Your answer should be a percent.) _____

i. Check: Show that the total interest is 10% of the total investments.

_____

Problem 3 A beaker contains 60 g of a solution that is 35% acid. How much pure acid should be added to produce a solution that is 50% acid?

a. What does the problem ask you to find? _____

_____

b. Complete: Pure acid = _____ % acid

c. Let a = the number of grams of pure acid to be added. Complete the chart.

	Total amount	×	% acid	=	Amount of acid
Original solution					
Added acid		a			
New solution					

d. Substitute the appropriate expression to write an equation:

Original amount of acid + added acid = new amount of acid

_____ + _____ = _____

e. By what number should you multiply both sides of the equation to eliminate the decimals? _____

f. Solve to find the value of a. _____

g. Answer the question. _____

(continued)

ALGEBRA, Structure and Method, Book 1

Mixture Problems *(continued)*

h. Check your answer by completing the following:

How many grams of acid are in the new solution? _____

What is the total number of grams in the new solution? _____

Is the new solution 50% acid? _____

Problem 4 Alloy A, which is 10% copper, is to be melted with alloy B, which is 40% copper, to produce 50 kg of an alloy that is 13% copper. How many kilograms of each alloy should be used?

a. Let x = the number of kilograms of alloy A. Write an expression for the number of kilograms of alloy B.

_____

b. Complete the chart.

	Total number of kilograms	$\times$	% copper	$=$	Number of kilograms of copper
Alloy A	x				
Alloy B					
New alloy					

c. Write an equation for the problem.

Copper in Alloy A + Copper in Alloy B = Copper in new alloy

_____ + _____ = _____

d. Solve your equation. _____

e. Answer the question. _____

_____

f. Check your answer by completing the following:

How many kilograms of copper in the new alloy will come from alloy A? _____

from alloy B? _____

Using the two answers you have just written, show that the new alloy is 13% copper. _____

_____

Work Problems (For use with Section 7–8)

By working through the steps in the problems below, you will gain skill in solving work problems.

Problem 1   A computer can process the Gonzales Electronics Company's payroll in 8 hours. An older back-up computer needs 10 hours to process the payroll. How long would it take the two computers working together to do the job?

a. What is the work rate of the faster computer? _____ job per hour

b. What is the work rate of the slower computer? _____ job per hour

c. Let h = the number of hours needed for the computers to do the job together. Complete the chart.

	Work rate	×	Time	=	Work done
Faster computer			h		
Slower computer			h		

d. To solve the problem, you use the fact that if a job is completed, the fractional parts of the job must have a

sum of _____ .

e. Write an equation for the problem. _____

f. Solve the equation. _____

g. Answer the question. _____

h. Check by completing the following.

Find the fractional part of the job done by the faster computer. _____

Find the fractional part of the job done by the slower computer. _____

What should the sum of these fractional parts be? _____ Is it? _____

Problem 2   Pipe A can fill an empty swimming pool in 4 hours, and pipe B can fill it in 6 hours. One day pipe A was temporarily out of order, so the pool manager started to fill the pool at 12:00 noon using only pipe B. At 1:30 P.M., when pipe A had been repaired, the two pipes were used to finish the job. At what time was the pool full?

a. What is pipe A's work rate? _____ job per _____

b. What is pipe B's work rate? _____ job per _____

c. Let x = the number of hours pipe A was used. Write an expression for the number of hours that pipe B

was used. _____

(continued)

ALGEBRA, Structure and Method, Book 1
Copyright © 1986 by Houghton Mifflin Company. All rights reserved. Printed in U.S.A.

Work Problems (continued)

d. Complete the chart.

	Work rate	×	Time	=	Work done
Pipe A			x		
Pipe B					

e. Write an equation, remembering that 1 represents the whole job.

_____

f. What is the LCD of the fractions in the equation? _____

g. Solve the equation. _____

h. The solution for the equation is in hours. Express it in hours and minutes. _____

i. Answer the question in the problem. _____

j. Check: Compute the parts of the job done by pipe A and by pipe B. Then make sure these parts have the required sum. _____

Problem 3   Ito can shovel his driveway in 2 hours. When his younger brother helps him, the driveway can be shoveled in just 72 minutes. How long would it take the younger brother to shovel the driveway alone?

a. Express 72 minutes in hours. _____

b. What is Ito's work rate? _____ of the job per _____

c. Let x = the number of hours it takes his younger brother to shovel the driveway alone. Write an expression for his work rate. _____ of the job per _____

d. Complete the chart.

	Work rate	×	Time (hours)	=	Work done
Ito					
Brother					

e. Write an equation. _____

f. What is the LCD of the fractions in the equation? _____

g. Solve the equation. _____

h. Answer the question. _____

i. Compute the parts of the job done by Ito and by his brother when they work together. Then make sure that these parts have the required sum. _____

Wind and Water Current Problems (For use with Section 8–8)

By working through the steps in the problems below, you will gain skill in solving two-variable uniform motion problems.

Problem 1 A canoeist travels with the current at 17 km/h and travels against the current at 6 km/h. Find the canoe's rate in still water and the rate of the current.

a. Let r = the canoe's rate in km/h (in still water), and let c = the rate of the current in km/h. Write an expression for the rate of the canoe when it is traveling downstream (that is, with the current). _____

b. Write an expression for the rate of the canoe when it is traveling upstream (that is, against the current). _____

c. Use the facts in the problem to write a system of two equations.

_____

_____

d. Solve for r. _____

e. Solve for c. _____

f. Write your answer to the problem. _____

g. Check: Show that the values for r and c yield results that agree with the original statement of the problem.

Canoe's rate with the current = _____ + _____ = _____

Canoe's rate against the current = _____ + _____ = _____

(continued)

ALGEBRA, Structure and Method, Book 1

Wind and Water Current Problems *(continued)*

Problem 2 It took a plane 50 min to fly the 330 km from Washington, D.C., to New York against the wind. The return trip with the wind took 5 min less. Find the speed of the plane in still air and the wind speed.

a. What unit should be used for the wind speed and the plane speed? _____

b. What unit should be used for flying time? _____

c. Express the flying time on the return trip using the appropriate unit. _____

d. Let r = the rate of the plane in km/h and let w = the rate of the wind in km/h. Complete the chart.

	Rate	×	Time	=	Distance
To New York					
To Washington					

e. Use the information in the chart to write a system of two equations.

_____

_____

f. Transform each equation by multiplication to eliminate the fractions.

_____

_____

g. Solve the system. r = _____ , w = _____

h. Write your answer to the problem. _____

i. Check your answer by completing the following.

How fast did the plane fly against the wind? _____

How fast did the plane fly with the wind? _____

Find the distance traveled on the trip to New York. _____

Find the distance traveled on the return trip. _____

The two distances should be equal. Are they? _____

(continued)

Wind and Water Current Problems *(continued)*

Problem 3 Lindsay can row 10 km/h in still water. She rowed downstream for 4 h. The return trip upstream took 6 h. How far did she row in all?

a. What formula should you use to solve this problem? _____

b. Let c = the rate in km/h of the current.

Rowing rate downstream = _____ (km/h)

Rowing rate upstream = _____ (km/h)

c. Let d = the distance in kilometers that Lindsay traveled downstream. Complete the chart.

	Rate	×	Time	=	Distance
Downstream					
Upstream					

d. Use the information in the chart to write a system of two equations.

_____

_____

e. What is the simplest method for solving this system?

_____

f. Solve to find the value of c. _____

g. Find the value of d. _____

h. Answer the question. (Reread it before you answer.)

_____

i. Check: What is the distance traveled on each part of the trip? _____ Are they

equal? _____

ALGEBRA, Structure and Method, Book 1

Digit Problems (For use with Section 8-9)

By working through the steps in the problems below, you will gain skill in solving digit problems.

Problem 1   The sum of the digits of a two-digit number is 11. If the digits are reversed, the new number is 45 less than the original number. What is the original number?

a. Let t = the tens digit of the *original* number.
Let u = the units digit of the *original* number.
Write an expression for the value of the original number. _____

b. Complete the chart.

	Tens	Units	Value
Original number			
New number			

c. Use the facts in the first sentence of the problem to write an equation.

_____

d. Use the facts in the second sentence of the problem to write another equation.

_____

e. Write the equation of part **d** in simplified form. _____

f. Use your equations from parts **c** and **e** to write a system of two equations.

_____

_____

g. Solve the system. $t =$ _____ , $u =$ _____

h. What is the original number? _____

What is the new number? _____

i. Answer the question in the problem. _____

j. Check your results with the statement of the problem.

What is the sum of the digits of the original number? _____

Which number is greater—the original number or the new number? How much greater is it?

_____

(continued)

Digit Problems (continued)

Problem 2 A two-digit number is eight times the sum of its digits. When the number is added to the number obtained by reversing the digits, the sum is 99. Find the original number.

a. Let t = the tens digit of the original number.
Let u = the units digit of the original number.
Write an expression for the value of the original number. _____

b. Complete the chart.

	Tens	Units	Value
Original number			
New number			

c. Use the facts in the first sentence of the problem to write an equation.

_____

d. Use the facts in the second sentence of the problem to write another equation.

_____

e. Write the equations of parts **c** and **d** in simplified form. You can use these simplified equations as your system of equations.

_____

_____

f. Solve the system of equations. $t =$ _____ , $u =$ _____

g. What is the original number? _____ What is the new number? _____

h. Answer the question in the problem. _____

i. Check your results with the original statement of the problem.

Show that the original number is eight times the sum of its digits. _____

Show that the sum of the original number and the new number is 99. _____

ALGEBRA, Structure and Method, Book 1

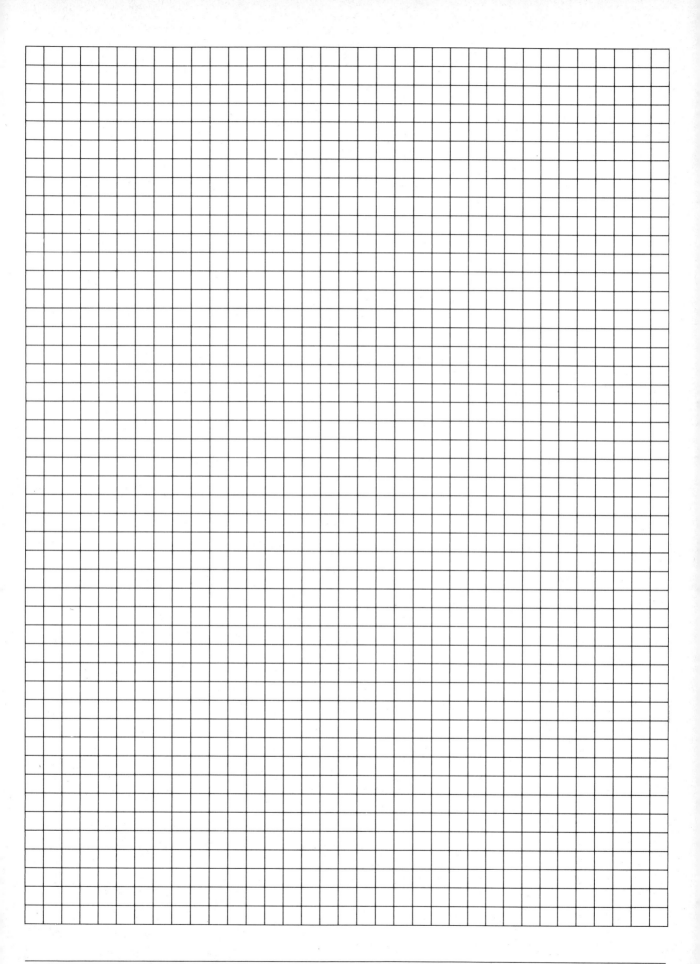

ALGEBRA, Structure and Method, Book 1
Copyright © 1986 by Houghton Mifflin Company. All rights reserved. Printed in U.S.A.

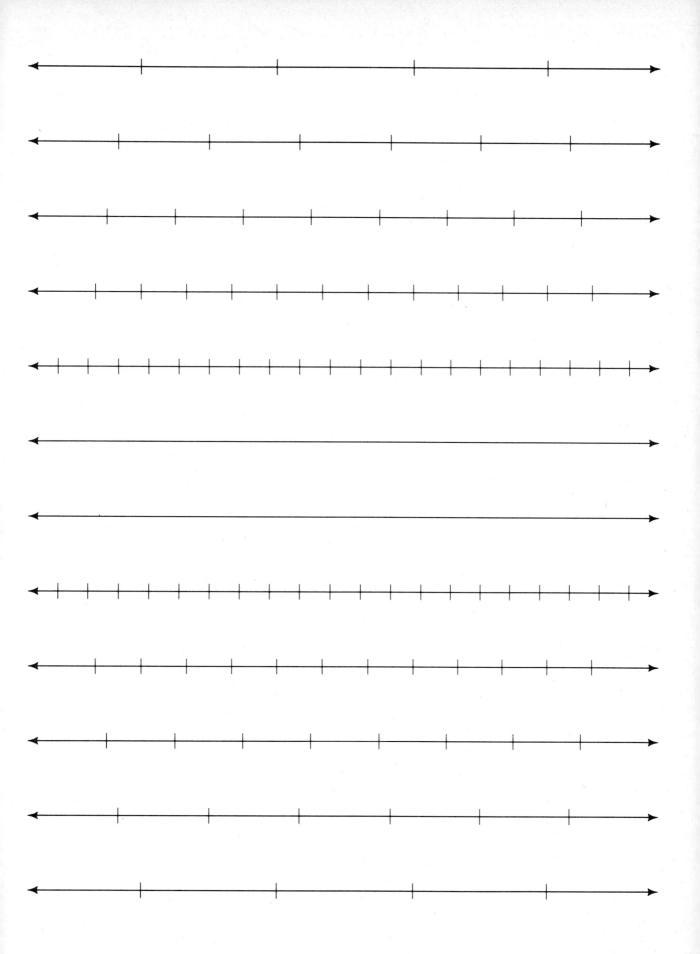

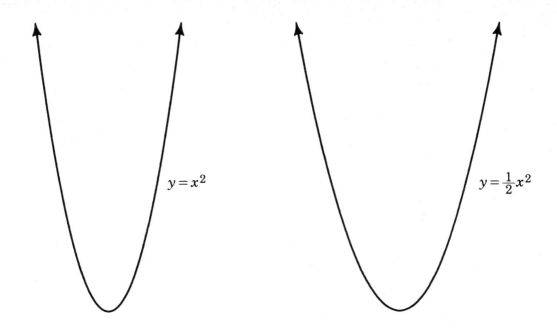

$y = x^2$

$y = \frac{1}{2}x^2$

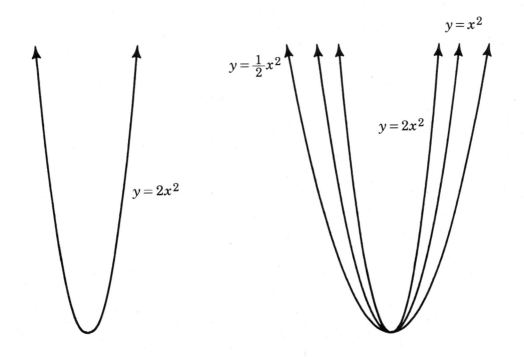

$y = 2x^2$

$y = \frac{1}{2}x^2$

$y = x^2$

$y = 2x^2$

Answers

Diagnostic Tests in Arithmetic

WHOLE NUMBERS **1. Addition** **1.** 98 **2.** 100 **3.** 91
4. 64 **5.** 149 **6.** 277 **7.** 271 **8.** 1451 **9.** 24,250
10. 12,488 **2. Subtraction** **1.** 31 **2.** 54 **3.** 8 **4.** 58
5. 423 **6.** 598 **7.** 693 **8.** 1304 **9.** 6899 **10.** 6796
3. Multiplication **1.** 92 **2.** 232 **3.** 780 **4.** 4480 **5.** 2254
6. 2814 **7.** 11,466 **8.** 2652 **9.** 24,324,000 **10.** 3,423,936
4. Division **1.** $146\frac{1}{3}$ **2.** $230\frac{1}{4}$ **3.** $253\frac{1}{3}$ **4.** $696\frac{2}{3}$ **5.** $174\frac{4}{23}$
6. $116\frac{7}{18}$ **7.** $209\frac{26}{29}$ **8.** $7\frac{23}{61}$ **9.** $58\frac{11}{14}$ **10.** $2\frac{373}{433}$

DECIMALS **1. Addition** **1.a.** 31 **b.** 25.6 **2.a.** 21
b. 21.28 **3.a.** 52 **b.** 47 **4.a.** 7.9 **b.** 7.725 **5.a.** 914
b. 945.5 **6.a.** 13 **b.** 14.086 **7.a.** \$939 **b.** \$940.40 **8.a.** 35
b. 30.76 **9.a.** \$26 **b.** \$25.06 **10.a.** 37.5 **b.** 36.12
2. Subtraction **1.** 5.50 **2.** 22.89 **3.** \$28.52 **4.** 2.0516
5. \$0.510 **6.** 599.5 **7.** 88.75 **8.** 67.16 **9.** 7734.92
10. 3876.95 **3. Multiplication** **1.** \$22.50 **2.** \$239.85
3. 53.17 **4.** 267.12 **5.** 0.021 **6.** 0.0054 **7.** 49.728
8. 28.75055 **9.** 1.5708 **10.** 101.03708 **4. Division** **1.** 9.1
2. 11.7 **3.** 13.7 **4.** 3.3 **5.** 17.9 **6.** 116.4 **7.** 0.2 **8.** 0.6
9. 3744.4 **10.** 0.2

FRACTIONS **1. Basic Ideas** **1.** 2 **2.** 4 **3.** 3 **4.** 9 **5.** 8
6. 3 **7.** 2 **8.** 100 **9.** 3 **10.** 2 **11.** 21 **12.** 7 **13.** $\frac{1}{7}$
14. $\frac{2}{5}$ **15.** $\frac{13}{45}$ **16.** $\frac{4}{9}$ **17.** $6\frac{2}{3}$ **18.** $8\frac{1}{10}$ **19.** $2\frac{1}{8}$ **20.** $4\frac{1}{2}$
21. = **22.** > **23.** > **24.** > **25.** < **26.** < **27.** 0.8
28. 0.9 **29.** 0.2 **30.** 0.3 **31.** $\frac{4}{5}$ **32.** $\frac{3}{4}$ **33.** $1\frac{3}{5}$ **34.** $1\frac{7}{8}$
2. Addition **1.** $\frac{7}{12}$ **2.** $\frac{5}{8}$ **3.** $1\frac{1}{6}$ **4.** $\frac{5}{6}$ **5.** $8\frac{3}{8}$ **6.** $16\frac{7}{9}$
7. $18\frac{3}{8}$ **8.** $13\frac{1}{6}$ **9.** $17\frac{7}{24}$ **3. Subtraction** **1.** $\frac{1}{8}$ **2.** $\frac{1}{16}$ **3.** $\frac{1}{4}$
4. $\frac{13}{24}$ **5.** $1\frac{5}{14}$ **6.** $3\frac{5}{8}$ **7.** $1\frac{7}{10}$ **8.** $4\frac{37}{40}$ **9.** $14\frac{7}{24}$ **4. Multiplication** **1.** $\frac{6}{7}$ **2.** $\frac{3}{14}$ **3.** 4 **4.** $\frac{1}{3}$ **5.** $\frac{1}{7}$ **6.** $2\frac{1}{4}$ **7.** $1\frac{1}{21}$
8. $4\frac{4}{8}$ **9.** $3\frac{7}{16}$ **5. Division** **1.** 4 **2.** 4 **3.** $1\frac{3}{4}$ **4.** $9\frac{3}{8}$ **5.** 26
6. 50 **7.** $1\frac{1}{9}$ **8.** 6 **9.** 2 **6. Ratios** **1.** $\frac{2}{5}$ **2.** $\frac{1}{3}$ **3.** $\frac{1}{4}$ **4.** $\frac{3}{2}$
5. $\frac{3}{4}$ **6.** $\frac{1}{20}$ **7.** $\frac{5}{1}$ **8.** $\frac{1}{3}$ **9.** $\frac{2}{25}$

PERCENT **1. Percents and decimals** **1.** 15% **2.** 65%
3. 1% **4.** 7% **5.** 25.5% or $25\frac{1}{2}$% **6.** 16.6% or $16\frac{2}{3}$% **7.** 250%
8. 575% **9.** 0.1 **10.** 0.05 **11.** 0.75 **12.** 1 **13.** 0.58
14. 0.015 **15.** 0.1075 **16.** 0.108 **2. Percents and frac-
tions** **1.** $\frac{1}{10}$ **2.** $\frac{1}{2}$ **3.** $\frac{9}{50}$ **4.** $\frac{49}{50}$ **5.** $\frac{11}{200}$ **6.** $\frac{51}{500}$ **7.** $\frac{177}{2500}$
8. $1\frac{1}{2}$ **9.** 50% **10.** 25% **11.** $16\frac{2}{3}$% **12.** 75% **13.** $12\frac{1}{2}$%
14. $87\frac{1}{2}$% **15.** 80% **16.** 36% **3. Percent Problems**
1. 10 **2.** 7 **3.** $37\frac{1}{2}$ **4.** 12 **5.** 10 **6.** $33\frac{1}{3}$ **7.** 1 **8.** 10
9. 30 **10.** 100 **11.** $5066\frac{2}{3}$ **12.** 39

Tests

TEST 1 **1.** 1 **2.** 90 **3.** 15 **4.** 3 **5.** 12 **6.** 0 **7.** $\frac{8}{35}$ **8.** 1
9. {2} **10.** {0, 2, 4} **11.** {6} **12.** $\emptyset$ **13.** $10 = \frac{x}{2} - 3$
14. $x + y - xy = 52$ **15.** 29 **16.** 18 **17.** 1700 **18.** $\frac{1}{2}$
19. -1 **20.** 1.5 or $\frac{3}{2}$ **21.** 19 **22.** 84 **23.** -3 **24.** <
25. = **Challenge:** 13

TEST 2 **1.** 49 **2.** 10 **3.** $\frac{1}{2}$ **4.** 9 **5.** 80 **6.** $\frac{13}{10}$ **7.** 13
8. 11 **9.** {1, 3, 5} **10.** {5} **11.** $\emptyset$ **12.** {3} **13.** $28 = 2m + 2$
14. $a + b + ab = 55$ **15.** 30 **16.** 21 **17.** 87 **18.** $\frac{3}{2}$ **19.** 0
20. -2.5 or $-\frac{5}{2}$ **21.** 10 **22.** -38 **23.** 40 **24.** < **25.** =
Challenge: 16

TEST 3 **1.** $20 - m$ **2.** -9 **3.** 5900 **4.** -5 **5.** -29
6. -1.4 **7.** $\frac{1}{2}$ **8.** She lost $4\frac{3}{4}$ pounds. **9.** 6 **10.** $-3a + 5$

11. 0 **12.** $-2n - 3$ **13.** $2a + 12b$ **14.** $4c - 1$ **15.** 0
16. -480 **17.** $x + (x + 1) + (x + 2) = 15$ **18.** $x = \frac{x + 1}{2} + 4$
19. $x(x + 1) = 110$ **20.** $(x + 1) + (x + 3) = (x + 2) + 17$ **21.** C
22. C **23.** $-c$ **24.** -9 **25.** -4.9 **26.** $\frac{5}{6}$ **27.** $0°$ **28.** B
Challenge: Axiom of opposites and identity axiom for addition

TEST 4 **1.** $12 - n$ **2.** -4 **3.** 7500 **4.** -7 **5.** 8 **6.** 1.0
7. $\frac{13}{5}$ **8.** down $\frac{1}{2}$ **9.** 0 **10.** $-r + 2$ **11.** 0 **12.** $-1.3d - 2$
13. $5p - 11q$ **14.** $a - 1$ **15.** 0 **16.** $-18,000$
17. $x + (x + 1) = 99$ **18.** $x + 1 = \frac{1}{2}(x) + 11$
19. $2(x) + 2(x + 1) = 82$ **20.** $4(x + 2) - \frac{1}{2}(x + 1) = 4$ **21.** C
22. B **23.** $-b$ **24.** -8 **25.** -32 **26.** $\frac{2}{5}$ **27.** \$6.40 average
gain **28.** C **Challenge: a.** Property of the opposite of a sum
b. Definition of subtraction

TEST 5 **1.** 7 **2.** 16 **3.** -60 **4.** -8 **5.** -40 **6.** 0.1 **7.** 3
8. 4.5 **9.** no solution **10.** -8.5 **11.** 7 **12.** 13 **13.** 600 at
20 cents, 400 at 25 cents **14.** $-1, 0, 1$ **15.** length = 225 m,
width = 100 m **16.** Tina is 4; her father is 28. **17.** B **18.** C
19. D **20.** A **21.** C **22.** B **23.** D **24.** A
Challenge: 3 lb. of grade A, 6 lb. of grade B, and
12 lb. of grade C

TEST 6 **1.** -3 **2.** 0.012 **3.** 1 **4.** $-\frac{2}{3}$ **5.** 40 **6.** 7.5
7. identity **8.** $\frac{1}{3}$ **9.** 6 **10.** no solution **11.** -42 **12.** 50
13. Sherry is 25; her son is 5. **14.** 241 at 25¢ each, 107 at 38¢ each
15. 0 and 2 **16.** 2 ft **17.** B **18.** D **19.** A **20.** C
21. A **22.** D **23.** E **24.** C **Challenge:** 60 1-cent stamps,
60 2-cent stamps, 10 14-cent stamps, and 30 22-cent stamps

TEST 7 **1.** -2 **2.** $\frac{3}{4}$ **3.** 3 **4.** -10 **5.** 12 **6.** 2.3 **7.** $5\frac{3}{8}$
8. 6 **9.** 12 **10.** 1 **11.** 2 **12.** $-7r - 11s$ **13.** y **14.** 4.1
15. 0 **16.** $-2\frac{1}{3}$ **17.** 0 **18.** 6 **19.** -6 **20.** $-1\frac{2}{3}$ **21.** 3
22. -3 **23.** 0 **24.** 6 **25.** -6 **26.** 7, -7 **27.** no solution
28. 2 **29.** -18 **30.** -8 **31.** 9 **32.** 45 **33.** identity
34. -3 **35.** -3 **36.** $2\frac{5}{8}$ **37.** no solution **38.** 2 **39.** 16
40. 0 **41.** 38, 40, 42, and 44 **42.** 38 of the 22-cent stamps and
12 of the 14-cent stamps **43.** 8 cm by 9 cm **44.** 7 and 12

TEST 8 **1.** $5y^3$ **2.** $(r + 2)^3$ **3.** $\frac{1}{2}g^2$ **4.a.** $4x^2 - 32x + 10$
b. $6x^2 - 10x - 2$ **5.a.** $4x^2 - 11$ **b.** $-2x^2 + 4x + 5$ **6.** $10x^5$
7. x^6 **8.** $-10a^3b^2$ **9.** $64m^4n^3$ **10.** $-9m^4n^6$ **11.** $\frac{n^7}{9}$
12. $-6a^2 + 12a - 6$ **13.** $-2a^3 + 6a^2$ **14.** $a^3 - b^3$ **15.** $a^3 + b^3$
16. $10x^2 + 17x + 3$ **17.** $9a^2 - 30a + 25$ **18.** $m = 2A - 22$
19. $b = \frac{P - 2h}{2}$ **20.** $x = -\frac{1}{2a}$ **21.** $h = \frac{2A}{a + b}$ **22.** 3 hours
23. no solution **24.** Sally, 15; Lynn, 10 **25.** freight, 40 mph;
passenger, 90 mph **26.** 12 cm by 16 cm **Challenge:** 26 mph

TEST 9 **1.** $(t + 7)^2$ **2.** $\frac{1}{4}h^5$ **3.** $8z^2$ **4.a.** $5x^2 - 3x - 8$
b. $9x^2 - 23x - 2$ **5.a.** $3x^2 + 20$ **b.** $-x^2 + 16x$ **6.** $-3x^5$
7. x^9 **8.** $-27a^3b^3$ **9.** $15xy^4$ **10.** $9m^2n^6$ **11.** $-16x^4y^2$
12. $-x^3 + 7x^2 + x$ **13.** $-2a^3 - 5a^2$ **14.** $m^3 - 27$ **15.** $m^3 + 27$
16. $20x^2 - 19x + 3$ **17.** $a^2 - 6ab + 9b^2$ **18.** $m = \frac{H - 2r}{3}$
19. $h = \frac{2W}{11} + 40$ **20.** $b = -\frac{4}{3a}$ **21.** $a = \frac{P}{2} - b$
22. 3:30 P.M. **23.** no solution **24.** Judy, 10; Rose, 15
25. Wally, 40 mph; Susan, 50 mph **26.** 13 cm by 15 cm
Challenge: 49.5 mph

TEST 10 **1.** $2 \cdot 3 \cdot 7 \cdot 13$ **2.** $2^3 \cdot 7^2$ **3.** 17 **4.** 16 **5.** $a^4 - 64$ **6.** $10e^6$ **7.** $42x^2 - 83x + 40$ **8.** $8n^2 - 4n + 5$ **9.** $25 - 9s^2$
10. $35x^2 - x - 6$ **11.** $\dfrac{-5}{21bc^2}$ **12.** $9x^2 + 12ax + 4a^2$
13. $-2n^3 + 3n^2 + 4n$ **14.** $c^2 - 8cd + 16d^2$ **15.** $-5a(x^2 + y^2)$
16. $(b - 8)(b + 3)$ **17.** $3y(2y - 1)(y + 1)$
18. $2(a^2 + 4)(a + 2)(a - 2)$ **19.** $(m + 6)(m + 15)$
20. $(3x - 2)(x - 1)$ **21.** $(g + m)(d - f)$ **22.** $(y + 24z)(y + 2z)$
23. $(7n - 1)^2$ **24.** $(x + 3)^2(x - 3)^2$ **25.** prime
26. $x^4(5x + 1)(5x - 1)$ **27.** $(b + 12)(b - 11)$ **28.** $(6x + 7)(x + 3)$
29. $(x - 2y + 3)(x - 2y - 3)$ **30.** $5(1 - 6y)(1 + y)$
31. $2(w^2 + 9)(w + 3)(w - 3)$ **32.** $-(n - 1)^2$ **33.** $\{-3, 5\}$
34. $\{-3, 8\}$ **35.** $\{-4, 0\}$ **36.** 6 and 8, or -8 and -6
Challenge: $h = 14$, $b = 9$

TEST 11 **1.** $2^2 \cdot 3^2 \cdot 7$ **2.** $3^2 \cdot 7^2$ **3.** 21 **4.** 35 **5.** $12y^2 - 34y + 24$ **6.** $\dfrac{-1}{mn^2p^3}$ **7.** $y^4 - 25$ **8.** $60w^2 + w - 10$ **9.** $-7s^4$
10. $r^2 - 16rs + 64s^2$ **11.** $25x^2 + 20xy + 4y^2$ **12.** $10r^2 + 2r - 7$
13. $36 - 25a^2$ **14.** $-8x^2 + 4x + 2$ **15.** $2v(3v + 1)(v + 4)$
16. $n(1 + n^2)(1 + n)(1 - n)$ **17.** $(3n - 1)(n - 1)$
18. $(x - 12)(x + 4)$ **19.** $(k + 11)(k - 10)$ **20.** $s^2(4 + s)(4 - s)$
21. prime **22.** $(a + 3b + 1)(a + 3b - 1)$ **23.** $(r + 30)(r + 3)$
24. $(s - t)(r - k)$ **25.** $-rt(t^2 + r^2)$ **26.** $(14x + 5)(x + 2)$
27. $-3(8y - 1)(y + 1)$ **28.** $a^2(a - 4)^2$
29. $3(m^2 + 9)(m + 3)(m - 3)$ **30.** $-(2b - 1)^2$
31. $(x + 12y)(x + 2y)$ **32.** $(5x - 2)^2$ **33.** $\{-3, 6\}$ **34.** $\{0, \frac{5}{2}\}$
35. $\{-3, 9\}$ **36.** 9 and 11, or -11 and -9
Challenge: $h = 8$, $b = 17$

TEST 12 **1.a.** $\dfrac{x - 4}{x - 3}$ **b.** $x \neq -2$, $x \neq 3$ **2.a.** $-\dfrac{c - 3}{c + 6}$
b. $c \neq 6$, $c \neq -6$ **3.a.** $-\frac{1}{2}$ **b.** $x \neq 7$ **4.a.** $\dfrac{3(a - 3)}{a + 1}$
b. $a \neq -1$, $a \neq -3$ **5.** $\frac{9}{25}$ **6.** $\dfrac{49x^8}{16}$ **7.** $\dfrac{a}{bc}$ **8.** $\dfrac{5rs}{7tu}$
9. $\dfrac{6h + 3}{12}$, $\dfrac{2h - 6}{12}$ **10.** $\dfrac{8ab + 12b^2}{12a^2b^2}$, $\dfrac{3a^2 + 6ab}{12a^2b^2}$, $\dfrac{2ab}{12a^2b^2}$
11. -1 **12.** $\dfrac{y - 1}{3x}$ **13.** $\dfrac{a^2 + 7a + 8}{a + 1}$ **14.** $\dfrac{2(x + 1)}{x + 2}$
15. $\dfrac{1}{m - 2}$ **16.** 1 **17.** $\dfrac{a + 4b}{b}$ **18.** $\dfrac{x - 2}{x + 1}$ **19.** 0
20. $\dfrac{25 + 15n - n^2}{5n}$ **21.** $x - 8$ **22.** $x^2 - 3x + 1 + \dfrac{1}{x + 4}$
Challenge: $\dfrac{a^2 + 3}{2a(a + 1)}$

TEST 13 **1.a.** $\dfrac{x - 3}{x + 3}$ **b.** $x \neq -3$, $x \neq 7$ **2.a.** $-\dfrac{2c + 1}{c + 3}$
b. $c \neq 3$, $c \neq -3$ **3.a.** $-\frac{5}{6}$ **b.** $x \neq 4$ **4.a.** $\dfrac{3(a - 4)}{a + 4}$
b. $c \neq -4$ **5.** $\frac{4}{9}$ **6.** $3x^4$ **7.** $\dfrac{a^2}{bc}$ **8.** $12r$ **9.** $\dfrac{9m + 3n}{15}$, $\dfrac{10n}{15}$
10. $\dfrac{a - b}{2a^2b}$, $\dfrac{2a^2}{2a^2b}$, $\dfrac{ab^2}{2a^2b}$ **11.** $-x$ **12.** $x^2(y - 1)$
13. $\dfrac{b^2 + 2b + 2}{b + 1}$ **14.** $\dfrac{x - 3}{x + 1}$ **15.** $\dfrac{n + 2}{(n + 1)(n - 1)}$ **16.** 1
17. $\dfrac{m - 3n}{n}$ **18.** $\dfrac{2x - 11}{x - 3}$ **19.** $\dfrac{-3(x - 2)}{x - 5}$
20. $-\dfrac{a^2 - 18a - 9}{3a}$ **21.** $4x - 2$ **22.** $2x^2 - 4x + 3 + \dfrac{2}{x + 3}$
Challenge: $\dfrac{a + 3}{a - 3}$

TEST 14 **1.** $-5x^4 + x^3 - 2x^2$ **2.** $m^2 + 6mn + 9n^2$
3. $t^5 + 2t^4 - t^3 - t^2 + 3t + 2$ **4.** $c^2 + 2$ **5.** 1 **6.** $12x^6y^6$
7. $13x^2 - 4x + 12$ **8.** $10m^2n^2 - 6mn + 1$ **9.** $13z + 3$
10. $\dfrac{c + 2d}{c - 2d}$ **11.** $216r^4$ **12.** $x^2 + 18x + 81$ **13.** $-x^2 + 3x + 1$
14. $15rs^2 + 20r^6s^3 - 5r^4s^6 - 35r^2s^9$ **15.** $62a^2b^2$ **16.** $\dfrac{1}{2(x - 5)}$
17. $x - y$ **18.** $\dfrac{z^2 + 5z + 13}{(z + 5)(z - 5)}$ **19.** $\dfrac{2a - b}{(a + b)(a - b)}$ **20.** $\dfrac{1}{x}$
21. $(a + 8)(a - 5)$ **22.** $4x(3x - 5)(x + 1)$ **23.** prime
24. $(x + 3)(x + 17)$ **25.** $a(z - 6w)^2$ **26.** $5rt(r - 2 + t)$
27. $(4r + 5t)^2$ **28.** $(3x - 1)(x + 7)$ **29.** $\{-9, 12\}$
30. $\{1, -1, 3, -3\}$ **31.** $\{0, \frac{1}{8}\}$ **32.** $\{2, -2\}$ **33.** $\{\frac{2}{3}, 5\}$
34. $\{0, -4, 10\}$ **35.** 8 and 9 **36.** 6 ft by 11 ft **37.** 35 km/h

TEST 15 **1.** T **2.** F **3.** F **4.** F **5.** T **6.** T **7.** F **8.** F
9. F **10.** T **11.** 0 **12.** 18 **13.** 2 **14.** $200x^5y^6$ **15.** 12.3
16. $4m^2 - n^2$ **17.** $9a + 28$ **18.** $\frac{1}{2}$ **19.** $4m^2 - 24mn + 36n^2$
20. $\dfrac{16h^2}{k^2}$ **21.** $-\dfrac{5c^2}{(c + d)^2}$ **22.** $6n^2 - 19n - 36$
23. $-15x^2y + 6x^3y^5 - 9x^4y^4 + 3x^2y^6$ **24.** $\dfrac{(x + 5)^2}{2(x^2 + 25)}$ **25.** $9n$
26. $\dfrac{x + 2}{x - 2}$ **27.** 0 **28.** $(x^2 + y^2)(x + y)(x - y)$ **29.** $(y + 5)^2$
30. $(x - 2y)(x + 3y)$ **31.** $(2x - 1)^2$ **32.** $(x - 9)^2$
33. $(3a + b)(2a - b)$ **34.** 2 **35.** -8 **36.** -4 **37.** -4 **38.** 0
39. 45 **40.** no solution **41.** -3 **42.** -5 **43.** 1 **44.** $\{0, -8\}$
45. $\{-5, -9\}$ **46.** $\{-3, -5\}$ **47.** 20 dimes and 32 quarters
48. Mike is 52; his daughter is 26. **49.** 9 miles **50.** 3, 4, 5, and
6 **51.** 2 and 10 **52.** 3 cm by 12 cm

TEST 16 **1.** $1:60$ **2.** $3:8$ **3.** $1:8$ **4.** $8:7$ **5.** $5:7$ **6.** 2.5
7. 9 **8.** -2 **9.** no solution **10.** $-\frac{9}{7}$ **11.** -7 **12.** 7
13. $-4, 6$ **14.** 15 hours **15.** 63 and 72 **16.** $80 **17.** $32.50
18. 32 gallons **19.** 75% **20.** $\dfrac{y^8}{4}$ **21.** 125 **22.** $\frac{1}{10}$
23. $\dfrac{a^6}{216b^9c^3}$ **24.** 375,000 **25.** 4.8×10^{-10} **Challenge:**
20 min

TEST 17 **1.** $5:6$ **2.** $3:5$ **3.** $5:14$ **4.** $1:2$ **5.** $3:1$ **6.** 9
7. $-\frac{1}{2}$ **8.** 1 **9.** 2 **10.** no solution **11.** 40 **12.** -5
13. $-1, 12$ **14.** $1\frac{1}{2}$ quarts **15.** $625 **16.** 24 hours
17. $1650 **18.** 20 and 44 **19.** 80% **20.** $\dfrac{x^8}{64y^{10}z^4}$
21. $\frac{1}{12}$ **22.** 81 **23.** 64 **24.** 17,900 **25.** 1.86×10^8
Challenge: 36 hours

TEST 18 **1.** yes **2.** no **3.** $y = -3x + \frac{3}{2}$ **4.** $y = \frac{7}{2}x + 1$
5. E, O, and B **6.** A and O **7.** F and O **8.** C, O, and G
9. 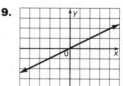 **10.**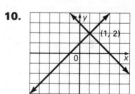
11. $m = 2$, $n = -3$ **12.** $x = 1$, $y = 5$ **13.** $c = 4$, $d = -\frac{1}{2}$
14. 20 boys, 15 girls **15.** 48 **16.** $3\frac{1}{2}$ mph **17.** $\frac{4}{9}$
Challenge: $\frac{39}{93}$

TEST 19 **1.** yes **2.** no **3.** $y = 7x$ **4.** $y = \frac{5}{2}x - 4$
5. F, G, and H **6.** D, E, and F **7.** F, O, and B **8.** H, O, and D

9. 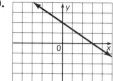   **10.**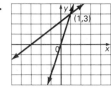

11. $w = 0$, $z = -2$ **12.** $x = 3$, $y = 1$ **13.** $p = -3$, $w = -7$
14. 120 boys, 180 girls   **15.** 95   **16.** $2\frac{1}{2}$ mph   **17.** $\frac{9}{12}$
Challenge: $\frac{24}{42}$

TEST 20   **1.a.** 3   **b.** 4   **2.a.** 1   **b.** 2   **3.a.** $\frac{2}{5}$ **b.** 0
4.a. 0   **b.** -6 **5.** $x = 3$ **6.** $y = 0$ **7.** $x - 3y = -6$
8. $x + 2y = 2$
9.a. $y = -\frac{3}{4}x + 3$ **10.a.** $y = -2x + 4$

b.   **b.**

11. yes   **12.** yes
13. yes   **14.** no
15. $\{1, 2, 3, 4, 5, 6\}$
16. $\{3, 5, 8, 9, 10, 12\}$

17. 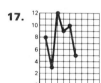   **18.**

19. 48 cm
20. $\frac{5}{16}$ ampere
21. 48
Challenge: $n = 6$

TEST 21   **1.a.** -7 **b.** 5   **2.a.** 1   **b.** 2   **3.a.** $\frac{4}{7}$ **b.** 0
4.a. 0   **b.** -1 **5.** $y = 1$ **6.** $x = 0$ **7.** $2x + 3y = 3$
8. $x - 2y = -7$
9.a. $y = x - 3$ **10.a.** $y = -\frac{3}{2}x + 2$

b.   **b.**

11. yes   **12.** yes
13. yes   **14.** no
15. $\{1, 2, 3, 4, 5, 6\}$
16. $\{3, 5, 7, 8, 12\}$

17. 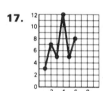   **18.**

19. 27 amperes
20. 22.5
21. 32 in³
Challenge: $n = 4$

TEST 22   **1.** $\frac{7a^2b^2}{11}$ $(a \neq 0, b \neq 0)$ **2.** 1 $(x \neq 0, y \neq 0)$

3. $\frac{2}{3g}$ $(g \neq 0)$ **4.** $2{:}1$ **5.** $\frac{2}{3}$ **6.** -7 **7.** $-2, 5$ **8.** $12\frac{1}{2}\%$
9. 200   **10.a.**

b. $x = 1$, $y = 2$
11. 3.664×10^9
12. $a = 9$, $b = 0$
13. $-\frac{3}{4}$
14. $x - 2y = 6$

15.a. $y = x - 2$ **b.**

16. 20%   **17.** 20 gal
18. 24 min and 48 min
19. 30 mph
20. Brian is 15; Matthew is 11.

TEST 23   **1.** $0 > -3$ **2.** $a \geq 2$ **3.** $-11 < -10$ **4.** $x \not> 0$
5. false   **6.** true   **7.** true   **8.** false   **9.** C   **10.** E   **11.** A
12. D

13.

14.

15.

16.

17.

18.

19. A   **20.**   **21.** C
Challenge: $\{-5, -3, -1, 1\}$,
$\{-3, -1, 0, 1\}$,
$\{-1, 1, 3, 5\}$, $\{1, 3, 5, 7\}$

TEST 24   **1.** $-1 > -2$ **2.** $b \leq 2$ **3.** $a \not< b$ **4.** $-5 < 0$
5. false   **6.** true   **7.** false   **8.** true   **9.** C   **10.** A   **11.** B
12. E

13.

14.

15.

16.

17.

18.

19. C   **20.**   **21.** D
Challenge:
$\{-12, -10, -8, -6\}$,
$\{-10, -8, -6, -4\}$,
$\{-8, -6, -4, -2\}$,
$\{-6, -4, -2, 0\}$,
$\{-4, -2, 0, 2\}$

TEST 25   **1.** $>$ **2.** $<$ **3.** $\frac{23}{48}$ **4.** $0.8\overline{3}$ **5.** 0.3125 **6.** $\frac{27}{99}$
7. $\frac{111}{250}$ **8.** 22   **9.** $\frac{13}{21}$ **10.** 22.45   **11.** 164   **12.** $6\sqrt{13}$
13. $5\sqrt{17}m^3n^5$ **14.** $\{\frac{3}{2}, -\frac{3}{2}\}$ **15.** no   **16.** yes   **17.** 7.62
18. 11.83   **19.** 12   **20.** 16.55   **21.** 7   **22.** $\frac{\sqrt{15}}{4}$ **23.** 3
24. $\frac{\sqrt{6}}{2}$ **25.** $6\sqrt{5}$ **26.** $15ab$ **27.** $-3 - 4\sqrt{3}$ **28.** $11 - 6\sqrt{2}$
29. $6 + 3\sqrt{3}$ **30.** $\frac{10\sqrt{3} - 5}{11}$ **31.** 26   **Challenge:** $\frac{80}{9}$

TEST 26   **1.** $<$ **2.** $=$ **3.** $\frac{19}{70}$ **4.** 0.375   **5.** $0.41\overline{6}$ **6.** $\frac{65}{99}$
7. $\frac{111}{200}$ **8.** 18   **9.** $\frac{1}{2}$ **10.** 23.24   **11.** 190   **12.** $10\sqrt{7}$
13. $16\sqrt{2}mn^4$ **14.** $\{\frac{5}{2}\}$ **15.** yes   **16.** no   **17.** 4.47   **18.** 11.62
19. 10.30   **20.** 12.69   **21.** 4   **22.** $\frac{\sqrt{3}}{4}$ **23.** $\frac{7}{2}$ **24.** $\frac{3\sqrt{2}}{2}$
25. $6\sqrt{7}$ **26.** $15ab\sqrt{a}$ **27.** $46 - 15\sqrt{2}$ **28.** $32 - 10\sqrt{7}$
29. $9 + 5\sqrt{3}$ **30.** $\frac{3\sqrt{5} + 1}{44}$ **31.** 4   **Challenge:** $\frac{15}{4}$

TEST 27   **1.** $(x - 6)^2$ **2.** $(x + 9)^2$ **3.** 49   **4.** $\frac{1}{4}$ **5.** $-3 \pm \sqrt{13}$
6. $-4 \pm \sqrt{11}$ **7.** $a = 5$, $b = -1$, $c = 3$ **8.** $\frac{-5 \pm \sqrt{17}}{4}$

9. no solution **10.a.** 13 **b.** 2 **11.a.** 0 **b.** 1 **12.a.** -3 **b.** none **13.a.** 5 **b.** 2 **14.** $\frac{15 \pm \sqrt{221}}{2}$ **15.** $\pm \frac{4\sqrt{3}}{3}$ **16.** $-4 \pm \sqrt{11}$ **17.** $\{0, 4\}$ **18.** $\{-3\}$ **19.** $\{1, 3\}$ **20.** 4 or -3 **21.** length = 15 cm, width = 12 cm **22.** 14 m **23.** Carla, 17.1 h; Anna, 15.1 h **24.** 30 **Challenge:** $m < -2$ or $m > \frac{6}{5}$

TEST 28 **1.** $(x - 10)^2$ **2.** $(x + 8)^2$ **3.** 225 **4.** 1 **5.** $-2 \pm \sqrt{2}$ **6.** $1 \pm \sqrt{2}$ **7.** $a = 3, b = -2, c = -1$ **8.** $\frac{1 \pm \sqrt{13}}{6}$ **9.** no solution **10.a.** 49 **b.** 2 **11.a.** -11 **b.** none **12.a.** 0 **b.** 1 **13.a.** 13 **b.** 2 **14.** $\{-5, 8\}$ **15.** $\{-5, 5\}$ **16.** $\frac{1 \pm \sqrt{5}}{2}$ **17.** $\{-4, -2\}$ **18.** $\{2, 3\}$ **19.** $\{-\frac{1}{6}, 1\}$ **20.** 15 **21.** length = 20 cm, width = 15 cm **22.** 20 cm **23.** Janice, 95 minutes; Roger, 105 minutes **24.** 35 **Challenge:** $-\frac{5}{2} < n < 3$

TEST 29 **1.** $2\sqrt{6} - 9$ **2.** $4\sqrt{2}$ **3.** $6\sqrt{2}$ **4.** $\frac{7\sqrt{10}}{30}$ **5.** $4\sqrt{2} + 6$ **6.** $45 + 20\sqrt{5}$ **7.** $10\sqrt{5}$ **8.** $\frac{\sqrt{2}b}{2a}$ **9.** $\sqrt{6} - 2$ **10.** 11 **11.** $\frac{\sqrt{3}}{5}$ **12.** 0 **13.** 2.3125 **14.** $\frac{297}{1000}$

15.a. $x > -5$ **b.**

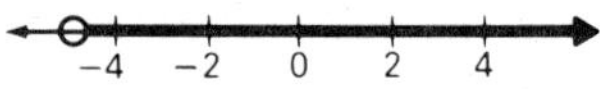

16.a. $-1 < x \leq 3$ **b.**

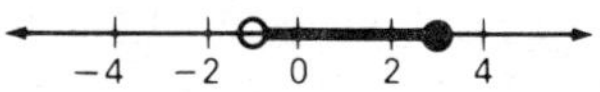

17.a. $-3 \leq x \leq 0$ **b.**

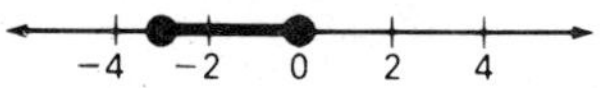

18.a. $x \leq -3$ or $x > 1$ **b.**

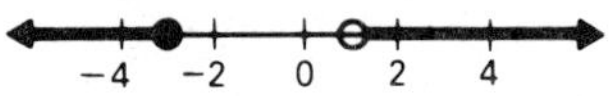

19. $\left\{\frac{-1 + 3\sqrt{5}}{2}, \frac{-1 - 3\sqrt{5}}{2}\right\}$ **20.** $\{3\sqrt{3}, -3\sqrt{3}\}$ **21.** $\{18\}$ **22.** $\left\{\frac{-5 + \sqrt{13}}{6}, \frac{-5 - \sqrt{13}}{6}\right\}$ **23.** $\{0\}$ **24.** $\{-8, -2\}$ **25.** $\{1, 3\}$ **26.** $\{0, 3, -3\}$ **27.** 6.3 cm **28.** 6 ft by 8 ft **29.** 40 minutes

TEST 30 **1.** $165 - 80\sqrt{3}$ **2.** 24:5 **3.** $10\sqrt{3}$ **4.** $\frac{4\sqrt{6} - 9}{3}$ **5.** $\frac{g^7}{3h^4}$ **6.** $\sqrt{2}$ **7.** $\frac{y - 2}{y + 2}$ **8.** $\frac{\sqrt{30}}{20}$ **9.** 140 **10.** -1 $(c \neq 0)$ **11.** 1.3×10^9 m **12.** $0.\overline{36}$ **13.** $\frac{26}{45}$

14.

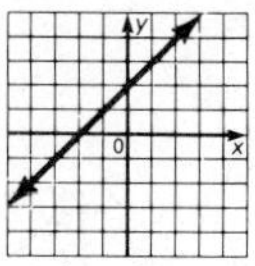

15.

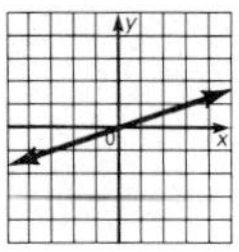

16.

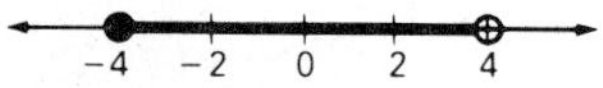

17.

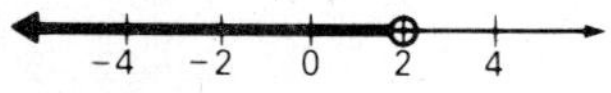

18.

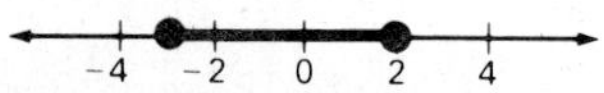

19.

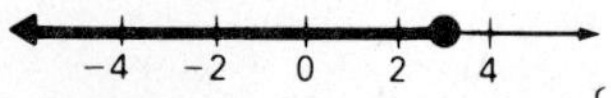

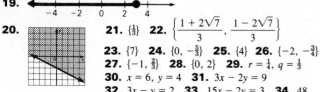

20.

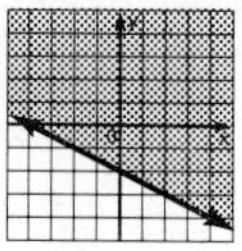

21. $\{\frac{1}{3}\}$ **22.** $\left\{\frac{1 + 2\sqrt{7}}{3}, \frac{1 - 2\sqrt{7}}{3}\right\}$ **23.** $\{7\}$ **24.** $\{0, -\frac{5}{3}\}$ **25.** $\{4\}$ **26.** $\{-2, -\frac{3}{4}\}$ **27.** $\{-1, \frac{2}{3}\}$ **28.** $\{0, 2\}$ **29.** $r = \frac{1}{4}, q = \frac{1}{3}$ **30.** $x = 6, y = 4$ **31.** $3x - 2y = 9$ **32.** $3x - y = 2$ **33.** $15x - 2y = 3$ **34.** 48 **35.** 10 L **36.** 35 **37.** $\frac{21}{28}$ **38.** 27 ohms **39.** 15 h

Practice Exercises

PAGE 67. **1.** times **2.** divided by **3.** $\neq$ **4.** grouping symbol **5.** 16 **6.** 3 **7.** 1 **8.** 3 **9.** 16 **10.** 48 **11.** 0 **12.** $\frac{3}{2}$ **13.** 1620 **14.** 17 **15.** 0 **16.** 78 **17.** 3 **18.** 7 **19.** = **20.** $\neq$ **21.** $\neq$ **22.** =

PAGE 68. **1.** root **2.** solution set **3.** domain **4.** 3 **5.** 6 **6.** no solution **7.** 6 **8.** $2n - 7$ **9.** $x + 8$ **10.** $x + 3 = 5$ **11.** $y - 5 = 2$ **12.** $3r + 16 = 64$ **13.** $4p = 96{,}000$ **14.** 10

PAGE 69. **1.** right **2.** whole **3.** negative **4.** -5 **5.** -2 **6.** 1 **7.** 4 **8.** *D* **9.** *G* **10.** *L* **11.** *A* **12.** 13 **13.** -11 **14.** 0 **15.** $\{-11, 11\}$ **16.** no solution **17.** $\{-5, 5\}$ **18.** $\{-1, 1\}$ **19.** $0 > -15$ **20.** $-2 > -3$ **21.** $<$ **22.** $>$ **23.** $<$ **24.** $<$

PAGE 70. **1.** A **2.** E **3.** B **4.** F **5.** G **6.** H **7.** C **8.** 430 **9.** 3700 **10.** 8.9 **11.** 16,800 **12.** $42a$ **13.** 41 **14.** 0 **15.** 6 **16.** 12 **17.** 2 **18.** 24 **19.** -25 **20.** -6 **21.** -5 **22.** 5 **23.** -9 **24.** 5 **25.** 1.6 **26.** -18 **27.** -4

PAGE 71. **1.** adding **2.** $-x - 7$ **3.** $ab + ac$ **4.** -7 **5.** 24 **6.** -6.4 **7.** -9 **8.** 0 **9.** -19 **10.** -9 **11.** -6 **12.** -10 **13.** -4 **14.** 10 **15.** $52n$ **16.** $-4c$ **17.** $7x + 36$ **18.** $3y + 7$ **19.** $-2t + 5$ **20.** $15a - 14b$ **21.** $5a + 2b$ **22.** $4x + 20$ **23.** $7y - 6$

PAGE 72. **1.** zero **2.** the opposite of the number **3.** negative **4.** positive **5.** $-12ab$ **6.** -990 **7.** 0 **8.** $-6c + 24$ **9.** $-10x + 15$ **10.** 540 **11.** $t - 2$ **12.** $-26x + 18$ **13.** $-x - 35$ **14.** *abcde* **15.** $5x - 5$ **16.** $y + 21$ **17.** $5n + 1$ **18.** $x + 11$ **19.** $x + (x + 1) + (x + 2) = 60$ **20.** $x + (x + 2) = 46$ **21.** $x + (x + 2) = 40$ **22.** $x + (x + 2) + (x + 4) + (x + 6) = 32$ **23.** $x + (x + 2) = 2(x + 1)$ **24.** $x + (x + 1) + (x + 2) + (x + 3) + (x + 4) = 0$

PAGE 73. **1.** 1 **2.** positive **3.** multiplicative **4.** $a \cdot \frac{1}{b}$ **5.** $\frac{5}{3}$ **6.** $\frac{1}{11}$ **7.** -3 **8.** 2.5 **9.** -1 **10.** -7 **11.** 9 **12.** $5a - 7b$ **13.** $a - 1$ **14.** $a - 2b$ **15.** 4 **16.** $25a$ **17.** 0 **18.** $-a$ **19.** 3 **20.** -147 **21.** 5 **22.** -28 **23.** -3 **24.** 1

PAGE 74. **1.** equivalent **2.** $b + c$ **3.** bc **4.** multiplication **5.** 15 **6.** 7 **7.** 10 **8.** 1 **9.** -8 **10.** 11 **11.** 8 **12.** 6 **13.** 2 **14.** 4 **15.** -48 **16.** -90 **17.** 8 **18.** 65 **19.** -24 **20.** -5 **21.** 5 **22.** 45 **23.** 20 **24.** -4 **25.** -1 **26.** 0 **27.** 2 **28.** $\frac{6}{5}$

PAGE 75. **1.** identity **2.** $x + 1$ and $x + 2$ **3.** 3 **4.** 1 **5.** 14 **6.** -2 **7.** -10 **8.** -5 **9.** identity **10.** no roots **11.** no roots **12.** 0 **13.** -2 **14.** no roots **15.** -11 **16.** -17 **17.** 35 **18.** identity **19.** 13 and 25 **20.** width is 10, length is 18 **21.** 16, 17, and 18

PAGE 76. **1.** Yolanda is 12; her mother is 48. **2.** 8 years **3.** Alex is 60; Jim is 12. **4.** 20 cm by 25 cm **5.** 21 **6.** 5 **7.** (1) given; (2) addition property of equality; (3) associative property of addition; (4) axiom of opposites; (5) addition property of zero

PAGES 77–78. **1.** 6 **2.** 6 **3.** 8 **4.** 47 **5.** -29 **6.** $-3a + 8b$ **7.** 3 **8.** -4 **9.** $7x - 3$ **10.** $5x + 3$ **11.** 4 **12.** 6 **13.** -5 **14.** 6 **15.** 0 **16.** -2 **17.** 0 **18.** -6 **19.** $x = -16$ **20.** $y = 9\frac{1}{2}$ **21.** $r = 54$ **22.** $x = 2$ or $x = -2$ **23.** $x = 11$ **24.** $x = 3\frac{2}{3}$ **25.** $y = 4$ **26.** $y = -4$ **27.** $m = 10$ **28.** $r = 5$ **29.** identity **30.** -75 **31.** no solution **32.** -8 **33.** $-6\frac{1}{2}, -6, \frac{5}{2}, 5$ **34.** $-2, -1\frac{1}{2}, 0, \frac{3}{4}$ **35.** 43 **36.** $28\frac{1}{2}$ **37.** -4 **38.** 8 **39.** 37 **40.** 37 and 39 **41.** 52 **42.** 21

PAGE 79. **1.** coefficient **2.** base **3.** binomial **4.** 5 **5.** 3
6. a^3 **7.** 2^2x^2 **8.** $-3x^4$ **9.** $(2y)^5$ **10.** $(-t)^2$ **11.** -200
12. 25 **13.** 288 **14.** 144 **15.** -144 **16.** 144 **17.** 1
18. -37 **19.** 16 **20.** $14x - 1$ **21.** $6c^2 + cd - 2d^2$
22. $8x - 6y$ **23.** $8n + 4$ **24.** $6x - 2y - 2$ **25.** $-2x^2 - 2$
26. $16n^2 - 4$ **27.** $x^3 - 6x^2 + 2x$ **28.** -8 **29.** $\frac{3}{4}$

PAGE 80. **1.** a^{m+n} **2.** a^{mn} **3.** c^{12} **4.** $-9y^8$ **5.** $30x^8$
6. $3125x^{25}$ **7.** $9y^9$ **8.** $5x^{25}$ **9.** $12a^4$ **10.** $25x^{10}$ **11.** $-210m^6$
12. $128y^7$ **13.** $25x^6$ **14.** $-36k^6$ **15.** $125x^6$ **16.** x^4y^4
17. $-26a^6$ **18.** x^8y^4 **19.** $14c^5$ **20.** $x^{12}y^8$ **21.** $14c^5$ **22.** $5a^8$
23. -4 **24.** 4 **25.** -2 **26.** 4

PAGE 81. **1.** $3x^3 - 12x^2 - 3x$ **2.** $-15y^2 + 5y^3$ **3.** $2a^3 -$
$a^2 + a$ **4.** $x^4y^2 - x^3y^2 + x^2y^4$ **5.** $-x - 6$ **6.** $-2x$ **7.** $-7x + 6$
8. $3x^3 - 13x^2$ **9.** -2 **10.** $-\frac{12}{5}$ **11.** 2 **12.** $\frac{9}{11}$ **13.** $x^2 -$
$13x + 42$ **14.** $x^2 + 13x + 42$ **15.** $3t^2 + 10t - 8$ **16.** $4c^2 -$
$4c - 15$ **17.** $3x^2 + 16x - 35$ **18.** $-2x^2 + 12x - 18$ **19.** $2a^3 -$
$7a^2 - 8a - 2$ **20.** $15x^4 - x^3 + 10x^2 + 4x$ **21.** $20c^2 - 22cd - 16d^2$
22. $15x^3 + 4x^2y - 9xy^2 + 2y^3$ **23.** $a^3 - b^3$ **24.** $9n^3 - 6n^2 +$
$7n + 10$ **25.** -1 **26.** $\frac{11}{6}$

PAGE 82. **1.** $h = \dfrac{2A}{b}$; $b \neq 0$ **2.** $t = \dfrac{I}{pr}$; $p \neq 0, r \neq 0$ **3.** $C =$

$\frac{5}{9}(F - 32)$ **4.** $n = \dfrac{2S}{a + 50}$; $a \neq -50$ **5.** $2\frac{1}{2}$ hours **6.** 420 miles

7. 9 mph and 18 mph **8.** 375 miles **9.** 300 yards

PAGE 83. **1.** 12 cm by 18 cm **2.** 324 cm² **3.** 20 m by
30 m **4.** no solution; the solution to equation must be a positive
whole number **5.** no solution; the sum of two odd numbers must be
even **6.** no solution; Laura's age cannot be 0 **7.** 44.4 mph (to the
nearest tenth) **8.** no solution; insufficient information

PAGE 84. **1.** $(1)(16), (2)(8), (4)(4), (-1)(-16), (-2)(-8),$
$(-4)(-4)$ **2.** $(1)(43), (-1)(-43)$ **3.** $2^2 \cdot 5^2$ **4.** $2 \cdot 3^2 \cdot 5^2$
5. 3^5 **6.** $2^5 \cdot 3^2$ **7.** 15 **8.** 32 **9.** 12 **10.** $\frac{5a}{4b}$ **11.** $\frac{3t}{r}$
12. -1 **13.** $9x^2y$ **14.** $-3ac^2$ **15.** a^5b^2 **16.** $5xy^5$ **17.** $x^2 +$
$2x - 3$ **18.** $6x + 7$ **19.** $y - y^2 - y^4$ **20.** $3 - xy^2$
21. $3x(3x - 5)$ **22.** $5x(x^2 - 2x + 1)$ **23.** $5x - 4$ **24.** 0

PAGE 85. **1.** $x^2 + 10x + 24$ **2.** $6c^2 - 25c + 24$ **3.** $y^2 - 2y -$
24 **4.** $x^2 - 5x - 14$ **5.** $2x^3 + 6x^2 + 4x$ **6.** $6x^2 + xy - 15y^2$
7. 3 **8.** -1 **9.** $x^2 - 49$ **10.** $9x^2 - 16$ **11.** $4c^2 - 25$
12. $a^4 - 4b^4$ **13.** $(13 + 2b)(13 - 2b)$ **14.** $(25a^2 + 12b) \cdot$
$(25a^2 - 12b)$ **15.** $(x^3 + 14)(x^3 - 14)$ **16.** $(11x + y)(11x - y)$
17. $4a^2 - 4ab + b^2$ **18.** $y^4 + 10y^2 + 25$ **19.** $9k^2 - 12km + 4m^2$
20. $9a^2 + 18ab + 9b^2$ **21.** $x^4 - 2x^2y^2 + y^4$ **22.** $x^4 + 2x^2y^2 + y^4$
23. $(x - 4)^2$ **24.** $(2a - b)^2$ **25.** not factorable **26.** $(3a - 2b)^2$
27. $3(2x + 3y)^2$ **28.** $a^3(a - 1)^2$

PAGE 86. **1.** $(y - 1)(y - 12)$ **2.** $(x + 9)(x - 2)$ **3.** $(y - 4) \cdot$
$(y - 3)$ **4.** $(j - 5)(j - 2)$ **5.** $(y - 6)(y - 2)$ **6.** $(5c - 1)(c + 1)$
7. $(y - 12)(y + 1)$ **8.** $(r + 14)(r + 2)$ **9.** $(y - 6)(y + 2)$
10. $(y + 6)^2$ **11.** $(y - 4)(y + 3)$ **12.** $(h - 9)(h - 3)$ **13.** $(x - 3) \cdot$
$(x - 1)$ **14.** $(a + 8)(a - 4)$ **15.** $(2y + 3)(y - 1)$ **16.** $(1 + 7d) \cdot$
$(1 + d)$ **17.** $(w + 11)(w + 3)$ **18.** $(d - 1)^2$ **19.** $(r - 11)(r - 2)$
20. prime **21.** $(p - 11)(p - 1)$ **22.** $(b + 13)(b - 7)$
23. $(4y + 5)(9y - 8)$ **24.** $(f - 8)(f - 2)$ **25.** $(3x - 2)(x - 3)$
26. $(2x + 5)(x - 7)$ **27.** $(b + 9)(b + 5)$ **28.** $(n + 16)(n + 3)$
29. $(a + 23)(a + 1)$ **30.** $(3x + 2)(3x - 1)$

PAGE 87. **1.** $10(x + 4)$ **2.** $4(y + 3)$ **3.** $4(y + 3)$ **4.** $(a - 2) \cdot$
$(b + c)$ **5.** $(x + y)(x + 1)$ **6.** $(b - c)(a - d)$ **7.** $(a - 3b)(2c - 3)$
8. $(4x - 3y)(2x + z)$ **9.** $(x + 2y)(4x - 1)$ **10.** $-3(x + 4)$
11. $(x + y - 3)(x - y + 3)$ **12.** $(a - b + c)(a - b - c)$
13. $(6a + 5)(4a - 5)$ **14.** $(3a + b + 2)(3a - b - 2)$
15. $5(c - 10)(c + 2)$ **16.** $(x^2 + 9)(x + 3)(x - 3)$

17. $8(x + 1)(x - 1)$ **18.** $x^2(y + 1)(y - 1)$ **19.** $3(x + 6)(x + 4)$
20. $(6x - 7y)^2$ **21.** $x(x + 12)(x - 12)$ **22.** $2(x + 30)(x - 25)$
23. $4(x - 1)^2$ **24.** $(a + 1)^2(a - 1)$ **25.** $x(x - 4)(x - 3)$
26. $(x^2 - 3)^2$ **27.** $2(y - 15)^2$ **28.** $5(2t - 5)(t + 1)$

PAGE 88. **1.** a or b **2.** linear **3.** quadratic **4.** $\{-8, -2\}$
5. $\{2, 6\}$ **6.** $\{-7, 7\}$ **7.** $\{-3, 7\}$ **8.** $\{0, \frac{11}{2}\}$ **9.** $\{-3, 5\}$
10. $\{-\frac{3}{2}, \frac{3}{2}\}$ **11.** $\{0, 2\}$ **12.** $\{-\frac{7}{2}, 3\}$ **13.** $\{-\frac{1}{6}, 0\}$
14. $\{-5, 12\}$ **15.** $\{-12, 0, 5\}$ **16.** $\{-\frac{3}{2}, 5\}$ **17.** $\{-1, -2, 3\}$
18. $\{-\frac{3}{2}, 4\}$ **19.** $\{-4, \frac{3}{2}\}$ **20.** $\{\frac{9}{5}, \frac{5}{2}\}$ **21.** $\{2, \frac{5}{2}\}$ **22.** $\{-1, 1\}$
23. $\{-5, 6\}$ **24.** 15 **25.** 11 and 13 **26.** 38 cm

PAGE 89. **1.** greatest common factor **2.** denominator **3.** -1;
$b \neq a$ **4.** 7; $x \neq 3$ **5.** $\dfrac{y + 4}{y - 4}$; $y \neq 4, y \neq -4$ **6.** $\dfrac{x}{y + 2}$; $y \neq -1$,

$y \neq -2$ **7.** $3 - a$; $a \neq 3$ **8.** $\dfrac{x + 5}{x - 5}$; $x \neq 5, x \neq 3$ **9.** 1; $y \neq \frac{4}{3}$

10. $\dfrac{3x - 1}{3}$; $x \neq \frac{3}{2}$ **11.** $\frac{11}{3}$ **12.** $\dfrac{c^2}{d^2}$ **13.** $\dfrac{5y}{x}$ **14.** $\dfrac{8x^2z}{7y^2}$

15. $27a^3b^6$ **16.** $\dfrac{4x^2}{y^2}$ **17.** $\dfrac{250a^3d}{c^2}$ **18.** $\dfrac{t(t - 2)}{2}$

19. $\dfrac{25x^2}{9}$ cm²

PAGE 90. **1.** $\dfrac{a}{b} \cdot \dfrac{d}{c}$ **2.** $\dfrac{x}{y}$ **3.** multiple **4.** $\frac{10}{3}$ **5.** $\frac{2}{3}$

6. $\dfrac{10b}{a}$ **7.** $x + 4$ **8.** -1 **9.** $\dfrac{(y + 3)(y - 3)}{(y - 1)^2}$ **10.** 2 **11.** -1

12. 24 **13.** $6xy$ **14.** $x + y$ **15.** $2y$ **16.** 24 **17.** $abcd$
18. $(x - 3)(x - 4)(x + 5)$ **19.** $3p(p - 3)$ **20.** $x^2 - 9$

PAGE 91. **1.** true **2.** true **3.** true **4.** false **5.** true
6. false **7.** true **8.** true **9.** $\dfrac{3x - 3}{7}$ **10.** $\dfrac{7y + 3}{y(y + 1)}$

11. $\dfrac{3 - x}{7}$ **12.** $\dfrac{7x - 15}{24}$ **13.** $\dfrac{3 - x}{x + 7}$ **14.** $\dfrac{x - 3}{8}$ **15.** $\dfrac{x + 7}{x - 7}$

16. $\dfrac{x^2 - 3}{7x}$ **17.** 1 **18.** $\dfrac{x^2 + 3x + 49}{7x}$ **19.** $\dfrac{x - 2}{x + 2}$

20. $\dfrac{5x - 8}{3(x + 4)(x - 4)}$ **21.** $\dfrac{11a - 53}{6}$ **22.** $\dfrac{12x - 3a + 4}{8}$

23. $-\frac{43}{8}$ **24.** $\dfrac{7x + 1}{x}$ **25.** $\dfrac{x - 5y}{y}$ **26.** $-\dfrac{x + 5}{x + 7}$

27. $\dfrac{58a - 55b}{30}$

PAGE 92. **1.** $x + 3$ **2.** $2x - 3$ **3.** $2q + 1$ **4.** $2x - 3 +$

$\dfrac{1}{2x - 7}$ **5.** $x^2 + 2x - 3$ **6.** $x + 5$ **7.** $2x - 7 + \dfrac{11}{x + 1}$

8. $x + 5 - \dfrac{2}{10x - 3}$ **9.** $x^2 + 3x + 9 + \dfrac{54}{x - 3}$ **10.** $x^2 - 3x + 9$

11. $x^3 + 2x^2 + 5x + 10$ **12.** $-9y - 3 + \dfrac{16}{2 - 7y}$ **13.** $x^2 - 6$

14. $x^2 + x - 1$ **15.** $x^2 - 4x + 4 - \dfrac{1}{2x + 1}$ **16.** $2x^2 - 11x + 15$

17. $x^2 + 2x - 3 + \dfrac{3}{x - 2}$ **18.** $x^3 - 1$ **19.** $x^2 + 2x + 4 + \dfrac{16}{x - 2}$

20. $x^2 - 2x + 4$ **21.** $x^4 + x^3 + x^2 + x + 1$ **22.** $x^2 - 12x + 36$
23. $n - 1$ **24.** $(n + 4)(2n - 5)(3n - 2)$

PAGES 93–94. **1.** 144 **2.** -48 **3.** 49 **4.** $\frac{1}{81}$ **5.** $5a - x$
6. $11a + 7x$ **7.** $-12x^3y^4$ **8.** $-432x^5y^8$ **9.** $4a^2b$ **10.** $2a^2b +$
$10ab^2$ **11.** $2a^2 + 11ab + 5b^2$ **12.** $x^2 - 9y^2$ **13.** $x^2 - 6xy + 9y^2$
14. $2a - b + 4$ **15.** $m = \frac{3}{4}$ **16.** $x = -\frac{1}{5}$ **17.** no solution
18. identity **19.** $m = -\frac{1}{2}$ **20.** $y = -20$ **21.** $y = -9$ or $y = -2$
22. $y = 0$ or $y = 5$ **23.** $y = -\frac{3}{2}$ **24.** $x = -3$ **25.** $\dfrac{9}{4a^3b^3}$

26. $-\dfrac{1}{3(x+4)}$ **27.** $7x+1$ **28.** $\dfrac{1}{2(x-4)}$ **29.** $-\frac{3}{2}$ **30.** x^2+
$x+1+\dfrac{2}{x-1}$ **31.** $\dfrac{5}{4x-2}$ **32.** $-\dfrac{y}{y+1}$ **33.** $\dfrac{25}{(r+5)^2}$
34. $\dfrac{x^2+1}{(x-1)(x+1)}$ **35.** $(y+9)(y+2)$ **36.** $3(2x^2+x+1)$
37. $(x-3y)(x+3y)$ **38.** $(2x+y)(x+5y)$ **39.** $(x-6)^2$
40. $12(x+1)(x-1)$ **41.** $(2y-1)(y+9)$ **42.** $2(x+4)(x-6)$
43. $(2+c)(a+b)$ **44.** $(r+2)^2(r-2)$ **45.** 40, 42
46. 32 **47.** 85 **48.** $5\frac{1}{2}$

PAGES 95–96. **1.** $4a$ **2.** $5a^2+15a-5ab$ **3.** $8a+2$
4. x^2-x-30 **5.** $3x-6$ **6.** $16m^4n^6p^2$ **7.** $2x^2-13x+15$
8. $4x^2-9$ **9.** $4x^2-12x+9$ **10.** x^3+3x^2+2x **11.** $-2\frac{1}{2}$
12. $2\frac{1}{2}$ **13.** -3 **14.** $-2\frac{1}{2}$ **15.** $-1\frac{1}{2}$ **16.** -10 **17.** $(x+3)\cdot$
$(x+4)$ **18.** $3(x+3)(x+4)$ **19.** $(2x+3)(x+5)$ **20.** $(2r-3)\cdot$
$(2r+3)$ **21.** $(y-6)(y+5)$ **22.** $x(x+4)(x-3)$ **23.** $4(y+5)\cdot$
$(y-5)$ **24.** prime **25.** $(y+5)(x+3)$ **26.** $(x+3)(x+1)\cdot$
$(x-1)$ **27.** $\dfrac{y^4}{5x^3}$ **28.** $-\dfrac{1}{2(c+1)}$ **29.** $\dfrac{8c+12}{(c-1)(c+1)}$
30. y^2 **31.** $x+5$ **32.** x^2+2x+4 **33.** $\dfrac{c}{2}$ **34.** $-\dfrac{1}{x}$
35. $\dfrac{-13}{(x+3)(x+4)}$ **36.** $\dfrac{y^2-2}{y^2+2}$ **37.** $x=-5$ **38.** $x=-8$
39. $x=3$ **40.** $x=2$ **41.** $y=-18$ **42.** $x=-7$ **43.** no
solution **44.** $m=8$ **45.** $x=0$ or $x=-\frac{1}{4}$ **46.** $y=\frac{43}{13}$ **47.** 31°,
59° **48.** width, 38 cm; length, 39 cm **49.** 400 mph, 430 mph
50. 6 and 7

PAGE 97. **1.** quotient **2.** ratios **3.** extremes **4.** $ad=bc$
5. 3:2 **6.** 3:4 **7.** 1:4 **8.** 10:1 **9.** 1:24 **10.** 3:26
11. 20:1 **12.** 3:40 **13.** 8:1 **14.** 2:3 **15.** $x=\frac{35}{6}$
16. $y=12$ **17.** $x=\frac{21}{10}$ **18.** $n=0$ **19.** $x=2$ **20.** $y=-\frac{2}{5}$
21. 20 and 24 **22.** \$8.40

PAGE 98. **1.** 7 **2.** $\frac{12}{5}$ **3.** $\frac{2}{5}$ **4.** 11 **5.** $\frac{2}{5}$ **6.** $\frac{12}{5}$ **7.** -15
8. 3 **9.** 63 and 27 **10.** 60 **11.** $\frac{40}{9}$ **12.** $\frac{10}{3}$ **13.** no solution
14. $\frac{2}{3}$ **15.** -3 **16.** 5 **17.** 42 **18.** $-\frac{1}{2}$ **19.** no solution
20. -12 **21.** $\frac{45}{4}$ **22.** 6 and 20

PAGE 99. **1.** hundredths **2.** multiplied **3.** original **4.** multiplied **5.** 18 **6.** 54 **7.** 2.16 **8.** 9 **9.** 15% **10.** 500
11. 160 **12.** 250% **13.** 21 **14.** 8 **15.** 24 **16.** 5
17. \$268.75 **18.** \$15 **19.** \$72.25 **20.** 15%
21. \$400 at 8%, \$200 at 12%

PAGE 100. **1.** 18 dimes, **2.** 225 minutes **3.** $22\frac{1}{2}$ seconds
4. 18 L **5.** 320 kg **6.** 16 kg **7.** 2 lb. wild rice, 8 lb. plain
rice **8.** 18.75 minutes **9.** 6 hours **10.** 24 km/h

PAGE 101. **1.** 10 **2.** 1 **3.** $\dfrac{1}{a^6}$ **4.** 5.0×10^6 **5.** 5.28×10^3
6. 1.0×10^{-6} **7.** 2.5×10^{-1} **8.** 3.45×10^{-3} **9.** 1.5×10^{12}
10. 3140 **11.** 9,010,000 **12.** 0.00301 **13.** 0.0086
14. 500,000 **15.** 0.00000000001 **16.** $\frac{1}{64}$ **17.** $\frac{1}{36}$ **18.** 625
19. $\frac{1}{729}$ **20.** $\frac{1}{7}$ **21.** 27 **22.** -1 **23.** $\frac{9}{82}$ **24.** $\dfrac{1}{y}$
25. 1.6×10^4 **26.** x^5 **27.** $\dfrac{1}{x^{11}}$ **28.** x^{11} **29.** $\dfrac{1}{x^5}$

PAGE 102. **1.** a pair of real numbers **2.** ordinate **3.** yes
4. yes **5.** no **6.** yes **7.** $y=2x$ **8.** $y=\frac{1}{3}x+2$ **9.** $(-1,2)$
10. $(0,5)$ **11.** $(4,3)$ **12.** $(3,-4)$ **13.** $(-4,-4)$ **14.** $(-5,1)$
15. H **16.** I **17.** K **18.** J

19.   **20.**

PAGE 103.
1. $(2,-2)$ **2.** $(2,2)$ **3.** $(0,0)$

4. $(-2,-4)$ **5.** no solution   **6.** $(2,1)$

7. $(3,3)$ **8.** $(3,9)$ **9.** infinite number of solutions **10.** $(3,-3)$
11. $(2,-7)$ **12.** $(11,-30)$ **13.** $(4,2)$ **14.** no solution

PAGE 104. **1.** 19 and 26 **2.** Wilma is 14. Her father is
42. **3.** $(5,5)$ **4.** $(1,5)$ **5.** $(2,0)$ **6.** $(2,-3)$ **7.** $(2,-3)$
8. $(1,5)$ **9.** $(-1,-3)$ **10.** $(4,-3)$ **11.** $(14,10)$
12. $(-4,-1)$ **13.** $(2,-3)$ **14.** $(-10,50)$ **15.** Liz is 15. Her
sister is 10.

PAGE 105. **1.** boat, 25 km/h; current, 4 km/h **2.** $393\frac{3}{4}$ m
3. $\frac{1}{2}$ hour **4.** 24 minutes **5.** 40 mi/h **6.** plane, 175 mi/h; wind,
25 mi/h **7.** 2 mi/h **8.** 20 km/h

PAGE 106. **1.** 78 **2.** 17 **3.** 152 **4.** 14 **5.** Millie is 24.
Maude is 36. **6.** 14 **7.** $\frac{35}{14}$ **8.** $\frac{10}{35}$ **9.** $\frac{7}{17}$

PAGE 107. **1.** $\dfrac{y_2-y_1}{x_2-x_1}$ **2.** equal **3.** vertical **4.** $-\frac{1}{2}$ **5.** -5
6. $-\frac{4}{5}$ **7.** $\frac{2}{3}$ **8.** -2 **9.** 1 **10.** -2 **11.** 0

12.   **13.**   **14.** 11 **15.** 7

PAGE 108. **1.** d **2.** a **3.** f **4.** e **5.** b **6.** $5x-y=2$
7. $2x-4y=-1$
8. $y=-\frac{1}{3}x+2$ **9.** $y=2x$ **10.** $y=x-1$

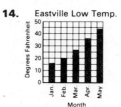

11. $2x-y=-3$ **12.** $2x-3y=0$ **13.** $2x-y=8$
14. $x-3y=-6$

PAGE 109. **1.** 20 **2.** 7 **3.** -4 **4.** -19 **5.** 7 **6.** 3
7. $-2\frac{1}{2}$ **8.** $3\frac{1}{4}$ **9.** 10 **10.** $R=\{11,5,2,-1,-7\}$ **11.** $R=$
$\{-3,0,1\}$ **12.** 1; $x=\frac{1}{3}$ **13.** 0; $x=0$ or $x=1$

14. Eastville Low Temp. **15.** Jogging Record

PAGE 110. **1.** line **2.** parabola **3.** minimum **4.** downward

5.   **6.**

7. vertex, $(-\frac{3}{2}, -\frac{9}{4})$;
axis of symmetry, $x = -\frac{3}{2}$

8. vertex, $(0, 4)$;
axis of symmetry, $x = 0$

PAGE 111. **1.** 540 **2.** 540 **3.** 225 **4.** $\frac{1}{4}$ **5.** The resulting square is 9 times as great. **6.** $5\frac{1}{3}$ feet **7.** The volume is 4 times as great. **8.** The number of revolutions is half as great.

PAGES 112–113. **1.** $\frac{3}{a^2}$ **2.** $\frac{x^4}{y^6}$ **3.** $4x^2 - 20x + 25$

4. $\frac{d-2}{2}$ **5.** $-x - 1$ **6.** $x^3 + 27$ **7.** $c = -16$ **8.** $c = -3$
9. $y = 6$ **10.** $y = -\frac{1}{4}$ **11.** $r = 6$ **12.** $x = 88$ **13.** $x = -2$
14. $y = 5$ or $y = 1$ **15.** $p = 10$ **16.** $x = \frac{56}{11}$ **17.** $x = -3$
18. $x = \frac{40}{3}$ **19.** $x = 2$ or $x = 7$ **20.** $x = 0$ or $x = 16$ **21.** $(1, 2)$
22. $(2, -3)$ **23.** $(3, 2)$ **24.** $(2, -4)$ **25.** 24 **26.** 300
27. $37\frac{1}{2}\%$ **28.** 125% **29.** 2.68×10^{-5} **30.** -2 **31.** $y = 3x - 6$ **32.** $y = 4x - 8$

33.   **34.**   **35.** -1
36. 30 barrels
37. \$102 **38.** 210
39. 36 minutes
40. 8

PAGE 114. **1.** $<$ **2.** $\geq$ **3.** negative **4.** negative **5.** c
6. a **7.** b **8.** d **9.** c
10. $r < 5$
11. $y \leq 1$
12. $x \leq 0$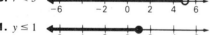
13. $x > 1$

PAGE 115. **1.** 40, 42 **2.** 87 **3.** 38 **4.** 105 **5.** \$16.99
6. 45 **7.** 27 cm **8.** 2 hours **9.** 100 gallons

PAGE 116. **1.** $-3 < x < 0$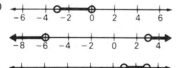

2. $x < -6$ or $x > 3$

3. $5 < x < 7$

4. $x \geq 7$

5. $x \leq 5$ or $x > 7$

6. $x < 7$

7. $-10 < x \leq -5$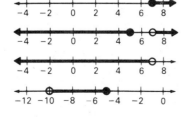

8. $-8 < x < -7$

9. $2 \leq x < 10$

10. $x \geq -5$

11. $-11 < x < -1$

12. $x > 2$

13. all real numbers

14. $0 < x < 6$

15. $\varnothing$ **16.** all real numbers

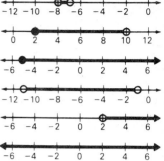
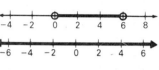
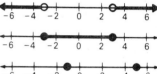
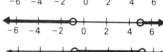
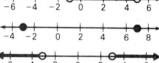
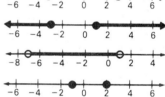
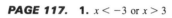

PAGE 117. **1.** $x < -3$ or $x > 3$

2. $-3 \leq x \leq 3$

3. $x = -1$ or $x = 5$

4. $x < -1$ or $x > 5$

5. $-1 < x < 5$

6. $x = -3$ or $x = 7$

7. $x < -3$ or $x > 3$

8. $x \leq -3$ or $x \geq 1$

9. $-7 < x < 1$

10. $x = -1$ or $x = 2$

11. $x = -\frac{1}{2}$ or $x = \frac{5}{2}$

12. $x = -2$ or $x = 2$

13. $x \leq \frac{4}{5}$ or $x \geq 2$

14. $x < -1$ or $x > 2$

15. $x \leq -2$ or $x \geq 10$

16. $-1 < x < 9$

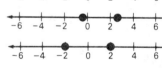
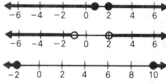

PAGE 118.

1.   **2.**   **3.**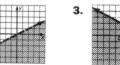

4.   **5.**   **6.**

ALGEBRA, Structure and Method, Book 1

7. **8.**

9. $y \le 2$
$x \le 2$

10. $y < -x + 2$
$y > -x - 2$

PAGE 119. **1.** integers **2.** density **3.** Rational **4.** All
5. $\frac{5}{6}, \frac{6}{7}, \frac{7}{8}$ **6.** $\frac{31}{34}, \frac{32}{34}, \frac{33}{34}$ **7.** $\frac{31}{36}, \frac{31}{35}, \frac{31}{34}$ **8.** $\frac{4}{7}, \frac{3}{5}, \frac{8}{11}, \frac{2}{3}$ **9.** $\frac{43}{60}$
10. $3\frac{5}{8}$ **11.** $-\frac{17}{200}$ **12.** 0.28 **13.** $0.\overline{714285}$ **14.** -3.125
15. $0.\overline{7}$ **16.** $\frac{27}{100}$ **17.** $\frac{25}{99}$ **18.** $\frac{17}{15}$ **19.** $\frac{1}{6}; \frac{5}{12}$ **20.** $\frac{1}{396}; \frac{199}{792}$

PAGE 120. **1.** nonnegative **2.** equals **3.** does not equal
4. decimal **5.** 4 **6.** 25 **7.** $\frac{15}{4}$ **8.** 17 **9.** $\frac{11}{2}$ **10.** $\frac{4}{13}$
11. 14 **12.** $9\sqrt{2}$ **13.** $5\sqrt{2}$ **14.** $10\sqrt{5}$ **15.** $7\sqrt{2}$ **16.** $3\sqrt{7}$
17. 14.1 **18.** 15.8 **19.** 70.7 **20.** 6.9 **21.** 26.5 **22.** 21.2
23. 9 and 10 **24.** 15 and 16 **25.** 11 and 12 **26.** 7 and 8

PAGE 121. **1.** y^2 **2.** $|x^3|$ **3.** $|t^5|$ **4.** $6\sqrt{2}|x|$ **5.** $11|x||y^3|$
6. $3\sqrt{5}y^2$ **7.** $7|y^3|$ **8.** $13|r^{11}|$ **9.** $3y^4$ **10.** $0.7|x|$ **11.** $25|x|y^2$
12. $|a||b^3|c^4$ **13.** $|x + 7|$ **14.** $|x - 4|$ **15.** $\{6, -6\}$
16. $\{90, -90\}$ **17.** $\{5, -5\}$ **18.** $\{-\frac{7}{6}, \frac{7}{6}\}$ **19.** $\{7, -7\}$
20. $\{8, -8\}$ **21.** 6.40 **22.** 2.45 **23.** 18 **24.** 3.61 **25.** 9
26. 11 cm **27.** 4.2 cm **28.** 80 in. **29.** yes **30.** no **31.** yes

PAGE 122. **1.** 18 **2.** $10\sqrt{3}$ **3.** $6\sqrt{2}$ **4.** 9 **5.** $30\sqrt{2}$
6. $\sqrt{3}$ **7.** 1 **8.** 4 **9.** $\frac{\sqrt{10}}{5}$ **10.** $\frac{\sqrt{6}}{6}$ **11.** $5\sqrt{3}$ **12.** $\frac{9}{4}$
13. $\frac{5\sqrt{2}}{2}$ **14.** 72 **15.** $-3ab\sqrt{ab}$ **16.** $15x^2$ **17.** $5\sqrt{5}$
18. $-\sqrt{6}$ **19.** $\sqrt{5}$ **20.** $\sqrt{7}$ **21.** $\sqrt{10}$ **22.** $\frac{5\sqrt{2}}{2}$ **23.** $9\sqrt{7}$
24. $3\sqrt{3}$ **25.** $-\frac{\sqrt{10}}{10}$ **26.** $x^3 + x^2$ **27.** -12 **28.** $\frac{x\sqrt{b^2 - a^2}}{ab}$

PAGE 123. **1.** -13 **2.** 62 **3.** -1 **4.** $19 - 8\sqrt{3}$ **5.** $66 +$
$16\sqrt{2}$ **6.** $11 + 2\sqrt{30}$ **7.** $10\sqrt{21} + 14\sqrt{3} + 20\sqrt{7} + 28$
8. $30\sqrt{2} - 6\sqrt{3}$ **9.** $\frac{20 - 5\sqrt{3}}{13}$ **10.** $\frac{\sqrt{15} + 4\sqrt{5}}{-13}$
11. $\frac{16 + 2\sqrt{2}}{31}$ **12.** $\frac{2\sqrt{2} + 16}{-31}$ **13.** $4\sqrt{3} - 6$ **14.** $-9 - 4\sqrt{5}$
15. 20 **16.** $12\frac{1}{2}$ **17.** 100 **18.** 20 **19.** $30\frac{1}{2}$ **20.** 21 **21.** -7
22. -22 **23.** 20 **24.** 5

PAGE 124. **1.** ± 6 **2.** $\pm\frac{4}{5}$ **3.** $\pm\sqrt{26}$ **4.** $\pm 5\sqrt{5}$ **5.** $-1, 7$
6. $-7, 1$ **7.** $3 \pm \sqrt{17}$ **8.** $-3 \pm \sqrt{6}$ **9.** $\frac{-4 \pm \sqrt{10}}{3}$
10. no solution **11.** $-\frac{3}{4} \pm \frac{\sqrt{2}}{2}$ **12.** $-5 \pm \sqrt{6}$ **13.** $-5, 7$
14. $-5, 1$ **15.** $0, -5$ **16.** $2, 5$ **17.** $-2, -5$ **18.** $1, \frac{5}{3}$
19. $1 \pm \sqrt{5}$ **20.** $-2 \pm \sqrt{2}$ **21.** $\frac{1 \pm \sqrt{5}}{2}$ **22.** $-4 \pm \sqrt{6}$
23. $8 \pm 6\sqrt{2}$ **24.** $1 \pm \sqrt{6}$ **25.** $\frac{-3 \pm 3\sqrt{5}}{2}$ **26.** $\frac{3 \pm \sqrt{21}}{2}$

PAGE 125. **1.** $1, -\frac{3}{2}$ **2.** $4, -3$ **3.** $-\frac{3}{2}, \frac{4}{5}$ **4.** $-1 \pm \sqrt{2}$
5. $3 \pm \sqrt{6}$ **6.** $-1, \frac{3}{5}$ **7.** $0, -\frac{5}{4}$ **8.** $\frac{-1 \pm \sqrt{61}}{6}$ **9.** $\frac{-2 \pm \sqrt{6}}{2}$
10. $0, \frac{3}{5}$ **11.** $\frac{-3 \pm \sqrt{5}}{2}$ **12.** $\frac{1 \pm 5\sqrt{5}}{2}$ **13.** $1, 4$
14. $\frac{1 \pm \sqrt{13}}{3}$ **15.** $-4 \pm 2\sqrt{5}$ **16.** $\frac{1 \pm \sqrt{41}}{20}$ **17.** 8
18. 2 or 3 **19.** 14 and 16 **20.** 20 feet by 30 feet

PAGE 126. **1.** -11; none **2.** 88; two **3.** 61; two **4.** 25;
two **5.** -23; none **6.** 0; one **7.** -12; none **8.** 16;
two **9.** two; up; below **10.** none; up; above **11.** one; up; on
12. none; up; above **13.** two; down; above

14. **15.**

PAGE 127. **1.** $-4, -5$ **2.** 4, 5 **3.** $\frac{-9 \pm \sqrt{201}}{2}$ **4.** $5 \pm$
$\sqrt{55}$ **5.** $\frac{1}{5}, -3$ **6.** $0, -\frac{14}{5}$ **7.** $0, \frac{1}{2}$ **8.** 4, 25 **9.** $\frac{1 \pm \sqrt{73}}{4}$
10. $3, -2$ **11.** $0, -5$ **12.** $\frac{1 \pm \sqrt{37}}{6}$ **13.** 12 or -13 **14.** 7
and 12 **15.** 16 m by 3 m, or 8 m by 6 m **16.** 23 m by 15 m
17. 9.1 hours

PAGES 128–129. **1.** $\frac{7}{11}$ **2.** $2\sqrt{6}$ **3.** $15\sqrt{5}$ **4.** $3\sqrt{3}$
5. $4\sqrt{21}$ **6.** $14 + 6\sqrt{5}$ **7.** 6 **8.** $3\sqrt{6} - 6\sqrt{3}$ **9.** $11x$
10. $-\frac{x^2y}{15}$ **11.** $x < 1$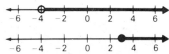

12. $x > -4$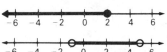

13. $x \ge 3$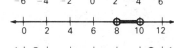

14. $x \le 2$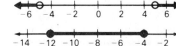

15. $-1 < x < 5$

16. $8 < x < 10$

17. $x < -5$ or $x > 5$

18. $-12 \le x \le -4$

19. $x = \pm 5$ **20.** $x = 4$ **21.** $x = 20$ **22.** $x = 3 + \sqrt{11}$ or $x =$
$3 - \sqrt{11}$

23. **24.** **25.**

26. **27.** 5 **28.** $5\sqrt{3}$ **29.** 0.35 **30.** $0.2\overline{3}$
31. $\frac{5}{8}$ **32.** $\frac{7}{11}$ **33.** 63, 65, 67 **34.** 48 m
35. -7 **36.** 74

PAGES 130–132. **1.** 3^3 **2.** $\frac{4^3}{x^6}$ **3.** $28\sqrt{3}$ **4.** 21
5. $7x^2\sqrt{5}$ **6.** $\frac{\sqrt{2}}{4}$ **7.** $12 + 6\sqrt{3}$ **8.** $\sqrt{3} + 1$ **9.** $y =$
$\frac{1 \pm \sqrt{33}}{2}$ **10.** $y = 2$ **11.** $x = 35$ **12.** $y \le \frac{-3}{34}$
13. $x = 7$ **14.** $x = 2$ **15.** $b = 20$ **16.** $x = 3$ **17.** $x = -2$
18. $-9 < x < -5$ **19.** $(-5, 0)$ **20.** $(2, -1)$ **21.** $(-6, 2)$
22. $(10\frac{1}{2}, 1\frac{1}{2})$ **23.** 2 **24.** $3x + 2y = 6$ **25.** $-x + y = 1$
26. 12% **27.** 0.25 **28.** 1:12 **29.** 1:400
30. $b = \frac{ad}{c}$ **31.** $0.8\overline{3}$ **32.** $\frac{8}{33}$ **33.** 2.05×10^{-5}

34.   **35.**   **36.**

15.   **16.** $(1, 1)$

37.   **38.**   **39.**

17. 50 **18.a.** $y + 4x = -23$ **b.** $4x - 5y = 7$ **19.** $y = 11$
20. $x = \frac{3}{2}$ **21.** $t = 6$ or $t = 1$ **22.** $z = 19$ **23.** $x = 5$
24. $n = 7$ **25.** $y = 6$ **26.** $x = 3$ **27.** $x = 2$ or $x = -7$
28. $x = \frac{3}{2}$ **29.** $x = 0, y = -3$ **30.** $x = 3, y = -1$
31. $(x - 11)(x + 11)$ **32.** $(x - 4)(x + 2)$ **33.** $(3n - 4)(2n + 1)$
34. $(3y - 2)(4y + 1)$ **35.** $(y + 11)(y + 12)$ **36.** $(3z^2 - 5)(3z^2 + 5)$
37. 7, 8 **38.** 18, 20 **39.a.** 3.8×10^{-4} **b.** $(3 \times 10^{-4}) +$
(8×10^{-5}) **40.** 80% **41.** $21\frac{1}{3}$ **42.** 62 **43.** $42 **44.** 85
45. 36 minutes **46.** 12 **47.** 57, 76, and 95 **48.** 50 cheese,
42 vegetarian **49.** $52 - k$ **50.** $-1, 1, 3$ **51.** $5 + (-2) > |-2|$
52. length, 14 cm; width, 7 cm **53.** 50 **54.a.** $f(0) = -2$
b. $f(-4) = -14$ **55.** $\dfrac{5x - 11}{x - 3}$ **56.** $7\frac{1}{2}$ **57.** no solution
58. 81, 84, 87 **59.** 540 km **60.** 4:30 P.M. **61.** 6 kg of the
$3.00/kg cereal, 9 kg of the $6.00/kg cereal **62.** $\dfrac{-27}{y^9}$ **63.** 6
64. $\dfrac{5x - 8}{6}$

40. length = 24 m, width = 12 m **41.** $16 **42.** 9, 10, 11 or
$-11, -10, -9$ **43.** 48

Mixed Review Exercises

PAGES 133–134. **1.** 1 **2.** 10 **3.** -11 **4.** 11 **5.** 2
6. -8 **7.** $p + 4p = 30$

8.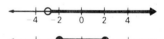

9. $n = -19$ **10.** $x = 7$ **11.** $y = 15$ **12.** $y = -45$ **13.** $q = 16$
14. $t = \frac{2}{3}$ **15.** no solution **16.** identity **17.** $|-5| > -(-3)$
18. $83 - t$ **19.** 20, 22, 24 **20.** -40 **21.** $13a + 21b$ **22.** -12
23. 0 **24.** 8 **25.** 660 **26.** -3.77 **27.** 119 **28.** 1 **29.** 56
30. $10t$ **31.** -32 **32.** $-2\frac{15}{16}, -2\frac{3}{4}, -2\frac{2}{3}, -2\frac{1}{8}$ **33.** 67 **34.** $>$
35. $<$ **36.** $x + (x + 2) + (x + 4) = 71$ **37.** 25 cm × 49 cm
38. R **39.** E **40.** A **41.** 14, 16, 18 **42.** 80

PAGES 135–137. **1.** $\frac{13}{41}$ **2.** 1 **3.** -6 **4.** 324 **5.** 10
6. 24 **7.** $x = 2$ **8.** $(\frac{1}{3}y)^4$ **9.** $36m^2$ **10.** $x = 5$ **11.** $y = 9$
12. $t = 7$ **13.** $m = -28$ **14.** $b = 3$ **15.** $y = 13$ **16.** $y = -8$
17. $x = -2$ **18.** 24 **19.** $(6t + 5)(t - 1)$ **20.** $(y - 11)(y + 5)$
21. $(4z + 3)(4z - 3)$ **22.** $3y(2y + 1)(2y - 1)$ **23.** $(x^2 + 11)^2$
24. $37xy^2(5xy^3 + 2y - 1)$ **25.** $\{2, 3\}$ **26.** $\{-\frac{3}{2}, \frac{3}{2}\}$ **27.** $\{-\frac{4}{3}, 5\}$
28. $\{-\sqrt{63}, 0, \sqrt{63}\}$ **29.** $2x^2 - 14x + 20$ **30.** $9y^2 - 4$
31. $-27x^{12}$ **32.** $3ab^4$ **33.** $5x^2 - 6x - 2$ **34.** $20x^3y^3$ **35.** 5
36. $\dfrac{t^2 + 6t + 2}{t(t + 1)}$ **37.** $7r^2st - 4s^2 + 8r^2s^2t^2$ **38.** $-32z + 12z^2$
39. $\dfrac{3y}{4x}$ **40.** $15n^3 - 22n^2 + 13n - 4$ **41.** $\dfrac{10x - 13}{12}$ **42.** t^{3+y}
43. $8a^2 - 3ab - 3a^2b^2$ **44.** -3 **45.** $\dfrac{(a - b)^2}{2a + b}$ **46.** $\dfrac{3y}{2y - 1}$
47. $225x^8y^8$ **48.** 26 **49.** 20 **50.** $8x + 5y$ **51.** $2 \times 2 \times 3 \times$
3×11 **52.** $m - 2 + \dfrac{3}{m - 1}$ **53.** $y^2 + y + 1$ **54.** 43 nickels, 73
dimes, 88 quarters **55.** 2000 km **56.** $\dfrac{3z - 2}{z + 1}$ **57.** $6xy^4$
58. 30 **59.** $x - 7$ **60.** $2y + 5$ **61.** $x + (x + 1) + (x + 2) =$
$4(x + 2) - 13$ **62.** $127.59°$ **63.** -24 **64.** 27, 28, 29
65. $(-1, -48), (-2, -24), (-3, -16), (-4, -12), (-6, -8)$
66. 5, 8 **67.** 4

PAGES 138–141. **1.** $14x - 10y$ **2.** 15 **3.** $\frac{3}{4}$ **4.** $\frac{1}{5}$
5. $\dfrac{-4y - 5}{y(y + 1)}$ **6.** $\dfrac{x^2y - xy^2 + 5x - 5y}{5y^2}$ **7.** $8r^{11}s^{12}$ **8.** $4t^2 - 9$
9. $x + x + 2 + x + 4 = 138$ **10.** 47 **11.** 275 kg **12.** 3
13. Jack is 23, Anna is 15 **14.** 9 and 24

PAGES 142–145. **1.** $6t^3 + 11t^2 + 2t - 8$ **2.** $x + 5$
3. $64x^{16}y^5$ **4.** 51 **5.** $\dfrac{b^2 - 11b - 8}{b(b + 1)}$ **6.** $\frac{4}{7}$ **7.** $6\sqrt{5}$ **8.** $12st^2\sqrt{t}$
9. $5\sqrt{7}$ **10.** $\frac{6}{5}x^3$ **11.** Alice, $3x + 7$; Archie, $x + 7$
12. 30 cm × 54 cm **13.** $(3x - 2)(x + 1)$ **14.** prime **15.** prime
16. prime **17.** $-(3x + 1)(16x - 15)$ **18.** $(3c + 4d)(c - 3d)$
19. 63 **20.** $3\frac{1}{2}$ h **21.** $\dfrac{4x - 4}{12}, \dfrac{3x}{12}, \dfrac{6}{12}$
22. $x > -3$
23. $-4 \leq x \leq 0$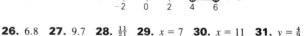
24. $z > 3$ or $z < 2$
25. $4 < t < 6$
26. 6.8 **27.** 9.7 **28.** $\frac{11}{21}$ **29.** $x = 7$ **30.** $x = 11$ **31.** $y = \frac{4}{9}$
32. $y < \frac{20}{9}$ **33.** $t = 4$ or $t = -4$ **34.** $t = -3$ **35.** $t > 2\frac{1}{2}$
36. $x = -7$ or $x = 1$ **37.** $x = 17, y = -10$ **38.** $x = 1, y = -1$
39. $3y - 14 + \dfrac{57}{y + 4}$ **40.** 42, 40 **41.** no real-number roots
42. one real-number root **43.** 14 **44.** 0.72 **45.** $0.8\overline{6}$ **46.** $1.\overline{4}$

47. **48.**

49. $110 + 7\sqrt{35}$ **50.** 18 **51.** $70 - 20\sqrt{10}$ **52.** $\frac{2}{3}$
53. $24\sqrt{3} - 15\sqrt{2}$ **54.** $3\sqrt{5}$ **55.** $x + y = -2$ **56.** $t =$
-1 or $t = -\frac{2}{3}$ **57.** $z = \dfrac{7 + \sqrt{17}}{4}$ or $z = \dfrac{7 - \sqrt{17}}{4}$
58. $4\frac{1}{3}$ **59.** -2 **60.** $9a^2c^2$ **61.** 3^6, or 729
62. $6 - \sqrt{3}, 6 + \sqrt{3}$

Enrichment Activities

PAGE 145. **1.** Pick a piece of fruit from the box labeled "apples and oranges." If it is an apple, then the box must contain only apples (not apples and oranges). Then the box labeled "oranges" must contain apples *and* oranges, and the box labeled "apples" must contain oranges. *Note:* A similar pattern of reasoning can be applied if the first pick yields an orange. **2.** Susan Teacher's child assists Mary Potter as a writer. **3.** 1980; anyone born in 1980 will be 45 in the year 2025 (45^2). **4.** Put three coins on one side and three on the other side. If they balance, then the odd coin is among the remaining two. If they don't balance, then the odd coin is among the three on the light side of the balance and can be found in a second weighing. **5.** 17¢ **6.** 5×12

PAGES 146–148. **1.** in the column headed by 0 **2.** in the column headed by 4 **3.** in the column headed by 16 **4.** in the column headed by 8 **5.** The sum is 4 times the selected number. To determine the selected number x, divide the sum by 4. $y = \frac{1}{4}s$, or $4y = s$. **6.** The numbers in the column headed by 4 are of the form $7n + 4$; and the numbers in the column headed by 5 are of the form $7n + 5$.
$$(7n + 4) + (7n + 5) = 14n + 9$$
$$= 14n + 7 + 2$$
$$= 7(2n + 1) + 2$$
$2n + 1$ must equal some integer k; so $7(2n + 1) + 2$ equals $7k + 2$; and $7k + 2$ is a number in the column headed by 2.

PAGES 149–150. **1.** $(x + 11) + (x + 7) = (2x + 1) + (x + 1) + (x + 2)$; $x = 7$ **2.** $(2x + 9) + (x + 9) + (x + 18) + (2x + 45) = (6x - 18) + (9x - 45)$; $x = 16$

PAGE 151. **1.** 3^3 or 27 **2.** M^N **3.** $x^3 - 1$ **4.** $x^4 - 1$ **5.** $x^5 - 1$ **6.** $x^{101} - 1$ **7.** $x^3 + 1$ **8.** $x^4 - 1$ **9.** $x^5 + 1$ **10.** $x^6 - 1$ **11.** $x^{101} + 1$

PAGE 152. **1.** $(1{,}234{,}567{,}890)(10{,}000{,}000{,}000)$ **2.** $1{,}000{,}000{,}000^2 - 11^2$ **3.** $-(1{,}234{,}567{,}889)^2$ **4.** $(975{,}308)(1{,}000{,}000)$ **5.** 1 **6.** $(3)(5) = 15 = 16 - 1 = 4^2 - 1$; $(7)(9) = 63 = 64 - 1 = 8^2 - 1$; $(11)(13) = 143 = 144 - 1 = 12^2 - 1$. Prediction: $(999)(1001) = 1000^2 - 1 = 999{,}999$. Let $x - 1$ represent the lesser of the two consecutive odd numbers; then $x + 1$ represents the greater of the two consecutive odd numbers. $(x - 1)(x + 1) = x^2 - 1$. Since x is the whole number between the two consecutive odd numbers, x^2 is a whole number and a perfect square. The product of $(x - 1)$ and $(x + 1)$ is 1 less than x^2; that is, it is 1 less than a perfect square. [Students' explanations may be less detailed and still be considered correct.] **7.** None of the three sums is divisible by 4. Prediction: $999 + 1000 + 1001 + 1002$ is not divisible by 4. Let x, $x + 1$, $x + 2$, and $x + 3$ represent any four consecutive integers. Then $x + (x + 1) + (x + 2) + (x + 3) = 4x + 6$. We can write $4x + 6$ as $4x + 4 + 2$, or $4(x + 1) + 2$. Since x is an integer, $x + 1$ is an integer. Let $x + 1 =$ the integer k. The sum of the four consecutive integers is $4k + 2$, and $4k + 2$ is not divisible by 4. (Only numbers of the form $4k$ are divisible by 4.) Thus, we have shown that the sum of four consecutive integers is not divisible by 4. [Students' explanations may be less detailed and still be considered correct.] **8.** $[BC]^2 + [B^2 + C^2][B + C]^2 = [BC]^2 + [B^2 + C^2][B^2 + 2BC + C^2] = [BC]^2 + B^4 + 2B^3C + 2B^2C^2 + 2BC^3 + C^4 = B^4 + 2B^3C + 3B^2C^2 + 2BC^3 + C^4 = (B^2 + BC + C^2)(B^2 + BC + C^2) = (B^2 + BC + C^2)^2$

PAGE 153. **1.** $\frac{2}{3}$ **2.** $\frac{8}{3}$ **3.** $\frac{8}{3}$ **4.** $\frac{32}{3}$ **5.** $\frac{1}{6}$ **6.** The expressions in Exercises 2 and 3 are equal; no, it is not a coincidence.
$$A/(B/(C/D)) = A \div \frac{B}{\frac{C}{D}} = A \div \frac{BD}{C} = A \times \frac{C}{BD} = \frac{AC}{BD}; \; (A/(B/C))/D$$

$$= \frac{A \div \frac{B}{C}}{D} = \frac{A \times \frac{C}{B}}{D} = \frac{\frac{AC}{B}}{D} = \frac{AC}{B} \times \frac{1}{D} = \frac{AC}{BD}.$$
The two expressions will always be equal.
7. $\frac{AD}{BC}$ **8.** $\frac{A}{BCD}$ **9.** $\frac{AC}{BD}$ **10.** $\frac{AC}{BD}$ **11.** $\frac{ACD}{B}$ **12.** The fractions in Exercises 9 and 10 are equal.

13. The fraction in Exercise 8 is equal to $\frac{A}{BCD}$. **14.** The fractions in Exercises 9 and 10 are equal to $\frac{AC}{BD}$. **15.** 11.25 **16.** 0.05

PAGE 154. **1.** $\frac{3}{2}$ **2.** $\frac{2}{3}$ **3.** $\frac{1}{a}$; the two expressions are reciprocals of each other **4.** 3 **5.** $\frac{1}{4}$

6.
$$\cfrac{1}{1 + \cfrac{1}{1 + \cfrac{1}{1 - \cfrac{1}{1 + \cfrac{1}{1 + \cfrac{1}{1}}}}}}$$

7.
$$\cfrac{1}{1 + \cfrac{1}{1 + \cfrac{1}{1 + \cfrac{1}{1 + \cfrac{1}{1 + \cfrac{1}{1}}}}}}$$

PAGE 155. **1.** $x = y = 5$ **2.** $x = y = 4$ **3.** $x = y = 1$ **4.** $x = y = 3$ **5.** $x = y = 0.1$ **6.** x and y can be interchanged and the equations will remain the same. **7.** $x = y = z = \frac{1}{2}$ **8.** $x = 1$, $y = 2$ **9.** $x = 8$, $y = -4$, $z = -3$ **10.** $x = \frac{5}{2}$, $y = \frac{9}{2}$, $z = 3$

PAGES 156–157.
1. 4, 16, 36, 64; $y = \frac{3}{2}x^2$

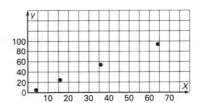

2. 1, 1.4, 1.7, 2; $y = 3\sqrt{x}$

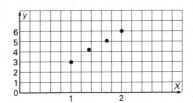

3. 9, 16, 25, 36; $y = \frac{2}{3}x^2$

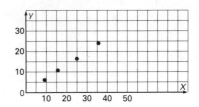

ALGEBRA, Structure and Method, Book 1

4.

x^2	4	16	36	64
y	0.5	2	4.5	8

$y = \frac{1}{8}x^2$

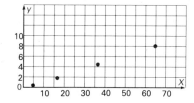

5.

$\frac{1}{x}$	0.33	0.20	0.14	0.11
y	1.67	1	0.71	0.56

$y = \frac{5}{x}$

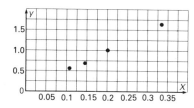

PAGE 158. **1.** Answers may vary. Possible answers include the following: $A = 3$, $B = 6$, $C = 2$ $(\frac{1}{3} + \frac{1}{6} + \frac{1}{2})$; $A = 12$, $B = 4$, $C = 3$ $(\frac{1}{12} + \frac{1}{4} = \frac{1}{3})$. **2.** $\frac{1}{xy}$ **3.** Since we know that $\frac{1}{x(x + y)} + \frac{1}{y(x + y)} = \frac{1}{xy}$, we can let $A = x(x + y)$, $B = y(x + y)$, and $C = xy$. By choosing different values for x and y, we can find various combinations of A, B, and C such that $\frac{1}{A} + \frac{1}{B} = \frac{1}{C}$. **4.** Answers may vary. Possible answers: $A = 2$, $B = 3$, $C = 6$, $D = 1$ $(\frac{1}{2} + \frac{1}{3} + \frac{1}{6} = \frac{1}{1})$; $A = 12$, $B = 4$, $C = 6$, $D = 2$ $(\frac{1}{12} + \frac{1}{4} + \frac{1}{6} = \frac{1}{2})$

PAGE 159. **1.** $20\sqrt{2}$ **2.** No. The ratio of the long sides is $\frac{17}{12}$; the ratio of the short sides is $\frac{12}{8.5}$; and $\frac{17}{12} \neq \frac{12}{8.5}$.

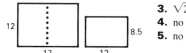

3. $\sqrt{2}:1$; no
4. no
5. no

PAGE 160. **1.** $a^2 + 2ab + b^2$ **2.** $2ab$ **3.** $\frac{b^2}{4}$
4. $\frac{1}{2}(a - b)(a + b)$; $(a + b)(a - b)$

Problem Solving

PAGES 161–162. **1.a.** the ages of Uncle Louis and Michelle now **b.** $x + 8$ **c.** $3x$ **d.** $3x + 8$

e.

	Age Now	Age in 8 Years
Michelle	x	$x + 8$
Uncle Louis	$3x$	$3x + 8$

f. $(x + 8) + (3x + 8) = 100$ **g.** $x = 21$; $3x = 63$ **h.** Michelle is 21. Uncle Louis is 63. **i.** yes, $63 = 3 \cdot 21$; yes, $(63 + 8) + (21 + 8)$ equals $71 + 29$, which is 100. **2.a.** California; 1990 **b.** $x - 90$ **c.** $x - 40$ **d.** $x - 130$

e.

	Age in 1990	Age in 1900
Calif.	x	$x - 90$
Idaho	$x - 40$	$x - 130$

f. $x - 90 = 5(x - 130)$ **g.** $x = 140$ **h.** By the year 1990, California will have been a state for 140 years. **i.** 50; 10; yes, since $50 = 5 \cdot 10$. California's age in 1990 will be 140, since $50 + 90 = 140$.

PAGES 163–164. **1.a.** how many containers of windshield washer fluid and ice scrapers Marina Perez bought **b.** $6 - x$

c.

	Number	× Price (dollars) =	Cost
Scrapers	x	0.69	$0.69x$
Fluid	$6 - x$	0.99	$0.99(6 - x)$

d. $0.99(6 - x)$; $0.69x$ **e.** $x = 2$; $6 - x = 4$ **f.** Marina bought 2 ice scrapers and 4 containers of windshield washer fluid. **g.** yes; $3.96; $1.38; $2.58 **2.a.** $n + 1$; $n + 2$; $3n + 3$ **b.** Number of bills × Value of each bill = Total value

c.

	Number	× Value	= Total Value
$20 bills	n	20	$20n$
$10 bills	$n + 1$	10	$10(n + 1)$
$5 bills	$n + 2$	5	$5(n + 2)$

d. The total value of all Chong Wun's bills is $440. **e.** $20n + 10(n + 1) + 5(n + 2) = 440$ **f.** $n = 12$

g.

	Number	× Value	= Total Value
$20 bills	12	$20	$240
$10 bills	13	$10	$130
$5 bills	14	$5	$70

h. Chong Wun has a total of 39 bills. **i.** yes; $440

PAGES 165–168. **1.a.** 1.3 h; 2.4 h

b.

	Rate	× Time	= Distance
Slower car	r	1.3	$1.3r$
Faster car	$r + 5$	2.4	$2.4(r + 5)$

c.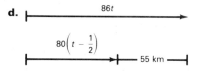

d. The faster car traveled twice as far as the slower car. **e.** $2(1.3r) = 2.4(r + 5)$ **f.** $r = 60$; slower car, 60 km/h; faster car, 65 km/h **g.** how far each car traveled **h.** The faster car traveled 156 km; the slower car traveled 78 km. **i.** Yes, $156 = 2 \cdot 78$ **2.a.** the time when the two cars were 55 km apart **b.** $t = \frac{1}{2}$

c.

	Rate	× Time	= Distance
Faster car	86 km/h	t	$86t$
Slower car	80 km/h	$t - \frac{1}{2}$	$80(t - \frac{1}{2})$

d.
$$86t$$
$$80\left(t - \frac{1}{2}\right)$$
$$\text{55 km}$$

e. $86t - 80(t - \frac{1}{2}) = 55$ **f.** $t = \frac{5}{2}$, or $2\frac{1}{2}$ **g.** the time when the cars were 55 km apart   **h.** 12:30 P.M.   **i.** At 12:30 P.M., $t = 2\frac{1}{2}$ and $t - \frac{1}{2} = 2$. $2\frac{1}{2} \cdot 86 = 215$; $2 \cdot 80 = 160$; $215 - 160 = 55$ **3.a.** $2j - 1$

b.

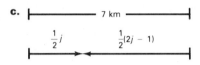

	Rate (km/h)	×	Time (h)	=	Distance (km)
Jenny	j		$\frac{1}{2}$		$\frac{1}{2}j$
Karen	$2j - 1$		$\frac{1}{2}$		$\frac{1}{2}(2j - 1)$

c.

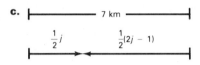

d. 7 km   **e.** $\frac{1}{2}j + \frac{1}{2}(2j - 1) = 7$ **f.** $j = 5$ **g.** no   **h.** $\frac{5}{2}$ km; $\frac{9}{2}$ km   **i.** 2 km   **j.** 7 km; yes   **4. a.** They must be equal.   **b.** No; since the rate upstream is less than the rate downstream, it will take more time to travel in the upstream direction.   **c.** $6 - x$

d.

	Rate	×	Time	=	Distance
Upstream	10		x		$10x$
Downstream	14		$6 - x$		$14(6 - x)$

e.

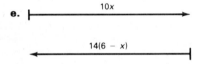

f. $10x = 14(6 - x)$ **g.** $x = 3.5$ **h.** how far upstream the boat traveled   **i.** 35 km   **j.** $10 \times 3.5 = 35$; $14 \times 2.5 = 35$; yes

PAGES 169–170.   **1.a.** $\frac{2}{3}x$

b.

	Length	×	Width	=	Area
First rect.	x		$\frac{2}{3}x$		$\frac{2}{3}x^2$
Second rect.	$x - 3$		$\frac{2}{3}x - 3$		$(x - 3)(\frac{2}{3}x - 3)$

c. $(x - 3)(\frac{2}{3}x - 3) = \frac{2}{3}x^2 - 66$ **d.** $x = 15$ **e.** 15 cm × 10 cm   **f.** Yes, $10 = \frac{2}{3} \cdot 15$. 150 cm²; 84 cm²; 66 cm²; yes   **2.a.** $x + 8$ **b.** $x + 1$ **c.** $x + 9$

d.

	Length	×	Width	=	Area
Inner rect.	$x + 8$		x		$x(x + 8)$
Outer rect.	$x + 9$		$x + 1$		$(x + 9)(x + 1)$

e. $(x + 9)(x + 1) - x(x + 8)$ **f.** $(x + 9)(x + 1) - x(x + 8) = 33$ **g.** $x = 12$ **h.** 20 m × 12 m   **i.** 240 m², 273 m², 33 m²; 273 − 240 = 33. 20 m is 8 m greater than 12 m.

PAGES 171–173.   **1.a.** 0; 100   **b.** Number of kg × Price per kg = Cost   **c.** $100 - p$

d.

	No. of kg ×	Price per kg =	Cost
Parmesan	p	\$3.50	$3.50p$
Romano	$100 - p$	\$5.00	$5.00(100 - p)$
Mixture	100	\$3.95	$3.95(100)$

e. cost of mixture   **f.** $3.5p + 5(100 - p) = 3.95(100)$ **g.** $p = 70$ **h.** 70 kg of parmesan and 30 kg of romano   **i.** \$245.00 + \$150.00 = \$395.00   **2.a.** 0.105; 0.10   **b.** Principal × Rate = Interest   **c.** Total Principal

d.

	Principal ×	Rate =	Interest
Certificate	1000	r	$1000r$
Bonds	4000	0.105	$4000(0.105)$
Total Investments	5000	0.10	$5000(0.10)$

e. Interest on the certificate + interest on the bonds   **f.** $1000r + 4000(0.105) = 5000(0.10)$ **g.** $r = 0.08$ **h.** an annual interest rate of 8%   **i.** $80 + 420 = 500$; $500 = 0.10(5000)$ **3.a.** the amount of pure acid that should be added to produce a solution that is 50% acid   **b.** 100

c.

	Total Amt. ×	% Acid =	Amt. of Acid
Original solution	60	35%	$0.35(60)$
Added acid	a	100%	a
New solution	$a + 60$	50%	$0.50(a + 60)$

d. $0.35(60) + a = 0.50(60 + a)$ **e.** 100   **f.** $a = 18$ **g.** 18 g of pure acid should be added.   **h.** 39 g; 78 g; yes   **4.a.** $50 - x$

b.

	Total No. of Kg ×	% Copper =	No. of Kg of Copper
Alloy A	x	10%	$0.10x$
Alloy B	$50 - x$	40%	$0.40(50 - x)$
New alloy	50	13%	$0.13(50)$

c. $0.10x + 0.40(50 - x) = 0.13(50)$ **d.** $x = 45$ **e.** 45 kg of alloy A and 5 kg of alloy B   **f.** 4.5; 2; $\dfrac{4.5 + 2}{50} = \dfrac{6.5}{50} = 0.13 = 13\%$

PAGES 174–175.   **1.a.** $\frac{1}{8}$ **b.** $\frac{1}{10}$

c.

	Work Rate ×	Time =	Work Done
Faster computer	$\frac{1}{8}$	h	$\dfrac{h}{8}$
Slower computer	$\frac{1}{10}$	h	$\dfrac{h}{10}$

d. 1   **e.** $\dfrac{h}{8} + \dfrac{h}{10} = 1$ **f.** $h = \frac{40}{9}$ **g.** It would take the two computers $4\frac{4}{9}$ hours to do the job.   **h.** $\frac{5}{9}$; $\frac{4}{9}$; 1; yes   **2.a.** $\frac{1}{4}$; hour   **b.** $\frac{1}{6}$; hour   **c.** $x + \frac{3}{2}$

d.

	Work Rate ×	Time =	Work Done
Pipe A	$\frac{1}{4}$	x	$\dfrac{x}{4}$
Pipe B	$\frac{1}{6}$	$x + \frac{3}{2}$	$\frac{1}{6}(x + \frac{3}{2})$

e. $\dfrac{x}{4} + \dfrac{1}{6}\left(x + \dfrac{3}{2}\right) = 1$ **f.** 12   **g.** $x = \frac{9}{5}$, or $1\frac{4}{5}$ **h.** 1 hour 48 minutes   **i.** 3:18 P.M.   **j.** pipe A, $\frac{9}{20}$; pipe B, $\frac{11}{20}$; $\frac{9}{20} + \frac{11}{20} = 1$, the required sum   **3.a.** $\frac{6}{5}$ hour   **b.** $\frac{1}{2}$; hour   **c.** $\dfrac{1}{x}$; hour

d.

	Work Rate ×	Time (hours) =	Work Done
Ito	$\frac{1}{2}$	$\frac{6}{5}$	$\frac{3}{5}$
Brother	$\dfrac{1}{x}$	$\frac{6}{5}$	$\dfrac{6}{5x}$

---

e. $\dfrac{3}{5} + \dfrac{6}{5x} = 1$ **f.** $5x$ **g.** $x = 3$ **h.** It would take the brother 3 hours. **i.** Ito, $\dfrac{3}{5}$; his brother, $\dfrac{2}{5}$; $\dfrac{3}{5} + \dfrac{2}{5} = 1$, the required sum

PAGES 176–178. **1.a.** $r + c$ **b.** $r - c$ **c.** $r + c = 17$; $r - c = 6$ **d.** $r = \dfrac{23}{2}$ **e.** $c = \dfrac{11}{2}$ **f.** The canoe's rate is $\dfrac{23}{2}$ km/h, and the rate of the current is $\dfrac{11}{2}$ km/h. **g.** $\dfrac{23}{2} + \dfrac{11}{2} = \dfrac{34}{2} = 17$ (km/h); $\dfrac{23}{2} - \dfrac{11}{2} = \dfrac{12}{2} = 6$ (km h) **2.a.** km/h **b.** hours **c.** $\dfrac{3}{4}$ h

d.

	Rate	×	Time	=	Distance
To New York	$r - w$		$\dfrac{5}{6}$		330
To Washington	$r + w$		$\dfrac{3}{4}$		330

e. $\dfrac{5}{6}(r - w) = 330$; $\dfrac{3}{4}(r + w) = 330$ **f.** $5r - 5w = 1980$; $3r + 3w = 1320$ **g.** $r = 418$, $w = 22$ **h.** The speed of the plane is 418 km/h, and the wind speed is 22 km/h. **i.** 396 km/h; 440 km/h; $396(\dfrac{5}{6})$ equals 330; $440(\dfrac{3}{4})$ equals 330; yes **3.a.** Rate × Time = Distance **b.** $10 + c$; $10 - c$

c.

	Rate	Time	Distance
Downstream	$10 + c$	4	d
Upstream	$10 - c$	6	d

d. $4(10 + c) = d$; $6(10 - c) = d$ **e.** substitution **f.** $c = 2$ **g.** $d = 48$ **h.** 96 km **i.** $12(4) = 48$; $8(6) = 48$; yes

PAGES 179–180. **1.a.** $10t + u$

b.

	Tens	Units	Value
Original number	t	u	$10t + u$
New number	u	t	$10u + t$

c. $t + u = 11$ **d.** $10u + t = (10t + u) - 45$ **e.** $9t - 9u = 45$, or $t - u = 5$ **f.** $t + u = 11$; $9t - 9u = 45$ **g.** $t = 8$, $u = 3$ **h.** 83; 38 **i.** 83 **j.** $8 + 3 = 11$; original number (83) is 45 greater than the new number (38) **2.a.** $10t + u$

b.

	Tens	Units	Value
Original number	t	u	$10t + u$
New number	u	t	$10u + t$

c. $10t + u = 8(t + u)$ **d.** $(10t + u) + (10u + t) = 99$ **e.** first equation, $2t = 7u$; second equation, $11t + 11u = 99$, or $t + u = 9$ **f.** $t = 7$, $u = 2$ **g.** 72; 27 **h.** 72 **i.** $72 \stackrel{?}{=} 8(7 + 2)$; $72 = 72$ $\checkmark$ $72 + 27 \stackrel{?}{=} 99$; $99 = 99$ $\checkmark$

For use after Section	Tests	Practice Exercises	Mixed Review	Enrichment Activities	Problem Solving
4-10		p. 83			
Chap. 4	pp. 19, 21			p. 151	
5-3		p. 84			
5-6		p. 85			
5-9		p. 86			
5-11		p. 87			
5-13		p. 88			
Chap. 5	pp. 23, 25			p. 152	
6-2		p. 89			
6-4		p. 90			
6-6		p. 91			
6-7		p. 92			
Chap. 6	pp. 27, 29			p. 153	
Cum. Rev. Chaps. 4-6	p. 31	p. 93			
Chaps. 1-6	p. 33	p. 95	p. 135		
7-2		p. 97			
7-4		p. 98			
7-6		p. 99			
7-7					p. 171
7-8		p. 100			p. 174
7-10		p. 101			
Chap. 7	pp. 36, 38			p. 154	
8-2		p. 102			
8-4		p. 103			
8-6		p. 104			
8-7		p. 105			
8-8					p. 176
8-9		p. 106			p. 179
Chap. 8	pp. 40, 42			p. 155	

For use after Section	Tests	Practice Exercises	Mixed Review	Enrichment Activities	Problem Solving
9-1		p. 107			
9-3		p. 108			
9-5		p. 109			
9-6		p. 110			
9-10		p. 111			
Chap. 9	pp. 44, 46			p. 156	
Cum. Rev. Chaps. 7-9	p. 48	p. 112			
Chaps. 1-9			p. 138		
10-2		p. 114			
10-3		p. 115			
10-4		p. 116			
10-6		p. 117			
10-8		p. 118			
Chap. 10	pp. 50, 52			p. 158	
11-2		p. 119			
11-4		p. 120			
11-6		p. 121			
11-8		p. 122			
11-10		p. 123			
Chap. 11	pp. 54-56			p. 159	
12-2		p. 124			
12-3		p. 125			
12-4		p. 126			
12-6		p. 127			
Chap. 12	pp. 58, 60			p. 160	
Cum. Rev. Chaps. 10-12	p. 62	p. 128			
Chaps. 7-12	p. 64	p. 130			
Chaps. 1-12			p. 142		